Mar. 16, "77"

W9-CZR-600

THEN CAME JESUS

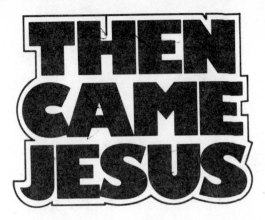

THEN CAME JESUS

Clyde A. Kirby

ZONDERVAN
PUBLISHING HOUSE
OF THE ZONDERVAN CORPORATION | GRAND RAPIDS, MICHIGAN 49506

*To my Friend and one of His friends
who helped make this book possible*

CONTENTS

Preface

PREFACE

What was it like in the upper room that fateful third day, the day of the resurrection of Jesus? No one this side of heaven can fully answer the question. It is likely that those who were there explored every height of hope, plumbed every depth of despair that day. In these eleven men with their doubts and longings, their faith and their hopes, there was the whole gamut of human emotions and need.

"Then . . . came Jesus and stood in the midst."[1] Then came Jesus! And suddenly their whole world was different. He was *there*. He was *alive*. What a vast transformation His presence wrought! He was Himself the answer to all their needs, the solution of all their problems.

And the wonder of it never ceases, for the Christ who came into the upper room still comes into human situations where hearts are burdened. Like a stream that flows with irresistible ease over and around all that stands in the way, that fills every crevice and pocket and hollow in its bed, so the joy of His presence flows out of the upper room where Jesus came and stood in the midst. Stony hearts have stood against Him only to be enfolded in His love. Sorrow and sadness that dammed up innumerable hearts have been swept away and gladness has taken their place. Sin-burdened souls have said, "No room for Thee" — still He comes and fills those souls with relief and release, with gladness and gratefulness. Into the midst of every human need He comes. Let a heart, any heart, be opened to Him and there He stands with the same tender concern, the same understanding, the same peace, the same power. Ever He shares the same victory that was His in the Resurrection.

Almost every pastor has a rich store of experiences where he has witnessed the coming of Christ into the heavy hearts and desperate hours of people. He has seen the renewed hope in eyes washed bright by tears when first a soul caught the faint sound of His footfalls. He has thrilled at newborn courage travailing its way up out of despair as the footsteps of Jesus came closer and a dawning realization of His nearness began to stir the depths of vanquished spirits. His heart has leaped with joy and then has prostrated itself in awe and adoration when Jesus came and stood in the midst.

It takes but one such hour to change a pastor's life forever. Having experienced this he can never be the same. From that matchless hour he goes forth with a love and compassion for people never before equalled in his life. But most of all he leaves that upper room with heights of praise and depths of certainty in him that before were beyond his reach. Once having been in some upper room of human need when "came Jesus" he knows that he need never fear to enter such a room with anyone. For the Christ who came then still comes there now, and he is utterly confident that the culmination will ever be — then came Jesus.

Out of one pastor's heart comes the sharing of a few of the times that he could say — "then came Jesus." This book is the setting forth of some of those transcendent moments. The pattern of the writing is to present "the Pastor" who many times and in many ways found the depths of his soul stirred as Jesus came and stood in the midst. Perhaps every minister, certainly every pastor, could multiply these experiences a thousand times over. As they read these pages they will understand them as perhaps others cannot, for they have been there when it could be said "then came Jesus." But the purpose of this writing will be realized only if all who read it will find herein the inspiration for a closer walk with Jesus and a greater willingness to be a door by which Jesus may come into the lives of others who are as desperately hungry for His presence as those lives were in the upper room on the eve of the Resurrection.

There only remains the need to say that "the Pastor" is a

real pastor and that the experiences set forth here are true. They are some of the many experiences upon which the writer can look back and say — "Then came Jesus."

¹John 20:19

THEN CAME JESUS

1

THE BIG
MEAN COP

OUTSIDE THE OPEN window a mockingbird poured out its greeting to the new day with outbursts of delirious joy. A robin, perched high in the great sugar maple in the front yard of the parsonage, tried vainly for awhile to tell the wakening world that his song was as sweet and clear as that of the mockingbird. Then it warbled a few notes in what seemed disgust and flew away to find breakfast. What finally broke through the curtain of sleep, though, and brought the Pastor to waking reality was the crow in the apple tree berating her mate for being so lazy. The man stirred sleepily, stretched, yawned a couple of times and climbed groggily out of bed.

The sweetness of the spring morning blowing its breath through the open window, the delirium of the mocking bird, the sounds stirring in the new day summoned him to the door. The beauty that sparkled on every hand was enough to catch at his throat. The hill across the way was a mixture of purple and gold; the shadows still lingered across a part of it as though fighting a delaying action with the lines of golden

13

light that marched row upon row. Behind every rock and tree the purple shadows hid and tried to cover themselves with the mist of morning; but their stay was short, for down the hillside swept the rays of the sun. Where the gold of the dawn touched the tender spring leaves, they turned a blushing pink.

Like a carpet of green velvet the grass mantled the hills, every dew-spangled blade sparkling golden in the rising sun. Behind the hill the artistry of the sunrise spread its glory across the sky.

The Pastor stood raptured, breathing deeply the clear, cool breath of morning. As always when he beheld the brush strokes of the Master Artist splashing upon the sky, his heart swelled with praise and thanksgiving. He murmured the old, old words, "The heavens declare the glory of God; and the firmament showeth his handiwork."[1] Before he turned back into the house, the prayer which began each day filled his heart once more. "O Lord, let me walk with Thee this day, for I give myself to Thee."

Soon the entire household was astir and the fragrance of bacon and coffee made a perfect compliment to the aroma of the apple blossoms that hung like clusters of pink-tinged snow from the boughs of the old tree just outside.

"I declare, kids," he said to the sleepy youngsters waiting at the kitchen table for the food to be placed before them, "I don't know which smells the best — outside or inside. But either one makes a man realize why the Lord put this protrusion that we call a nose in the middle of our faces."

Thus began a day in the Pastor's life that was to mark the opening of a wonderful story, another time when he would say with a heart aflame with praise — "Then came Jesus."

But it didn't seem to be that kind of a story at first. In fact, the opening stages of it brought a red face of shame and downright humiliation. Later that morning the Pastor was on the way to his study at the church. There were letters to be mailed, so he stopped at the post office on Main Street. As in

14

most cities, there were signs in front of the post office denoting a ten-minute parking area. Certainly there was no expectation of being gone but a minute or two when he pulled over to the curb and stepped out. Once inside the lobby, however, it was a different story. True, the place was not crowded as it would be later at mail delivery time, but most of the people who were there wanted to pass a few words with the new minister.

"Reverend, how do you think you are going to like living here?"

"Oh, we have already found it a delightful place, thank you."

"Preacher, you are going to find you have some tough nuts to crack if you think you are going to make everybody in this town get religion."

"Is that right? We have found the people to be most cordial, so far."

"Hey, Reverend," this was from a thin-faced youth. "You got any daughters? The last preacher had a couple of beauties, but they were sort of stuck up. If you have any girls, I expect you'll see me around the parsonage."

"Well, Bub, there are no daughters yet, but we have a couple of sons who would be glad to make your acquaintance."

So it went. The warm friendliness and genuine interest of the people he met washed over the pastor and he thought, *These are my kind of people. Everyday I am more grateful to God that He brought us to this beautiful place.*

That is the way it was on the inside of the post office that delightful spring morning. But on the outside some things were different. As the Pastor emerged, long past the ten-minute allotment, he saw the burly, blue-clad policeman leaning with his elbow on the ten-minute parking sign. The scowling face alternately looked toward the post office door and at the watch that seemed no bigger than a quarter in the

15

palm of his huge hand. A little prickle of apprehension went up the Pastor's spine as he noted the situation before him.

"Maybe this is one of the tough nuts that fellow spoke of a moment ago," he thought as he walked toward his car. Aloud he said as he drew near, "Good morning, officer."

There was no affable greeting in reply. The scowl on the red face deepened if anything. The policeman glared again at his watch and then growled in a gravelly voice, "Is this your car, mister?"

"Yes, sir, it is mine. Why? Am I overparked? If so, I am sorry."

"Overparked?" The voice dripped with sarcasm. "Mister, who do you think you are? Can't you read? This sign says ten minutes. In case you can't count, or tell time, you got ten fingers you can count on. You must think you are a privileged character. Maybe I should call you 'Your Honor' or something, or maybe you are the Postmaster General of the United States."

Now, the Pastor had never been noted for possessing too great an abundance of meek submissiveness. More than once some church member, bent upon giving a tongue-lashing to a supposedly meek and defenseless minister, had trailed off to disturbed and astonished silence when suddenly a flame leaped into the Pastor's usually friendly eyes. Seldom did he allow himself to speak at such a time, but he knew — and others who knew him soon came to realize — that here was one preacher nobody pushed around. Therefore as the sarcastic voice reeled on and on in the furious lecture, the Pastor was struggling within himself at the abuse and quietly praying as did the psalmist of old, "Set a watch, O Lord, before my mouth."[2]

When at last there came a brief lull in the waves of abuse, he spoke with the usual quiet friendliness. "I am sorry, officer. You see, I have only lived here for a few days, and I am still interested in meeting the citizens of your lovely

16

town. I suppose I lost track of the time on that account. It won't happen again.''

Somewhat mollified by the apology, the officer started to turn away. He paused for a parting shot. ''The next time, Mister, I don't care who you are, you get a ticket. By the way, who are you?''

''I am the Pastor who has just come here.''

''Huh!'' The sarcasm now changed to disgust. ''I might have known it; a preacher! You guys never do anything but make trouble anyway.'' And with that he turned and stalked up Main Street.

While all of this was happening several spectators had gathered a few feet away to watch and listen. Some of them moved closer to the Pastor now. The others went on their way.

''Who was that officer?'' the Pastor inquired.

''Oh, that's our prize policeman,'' came the reply. ''His name is Brame. He's quite a guy. You had better stay clear of him, Preacher. If that boy gets down on you, yours will be a hard road to travel.''

Still smarting from the experience, the Pastor drove away. The disturbance in his mind was not altogether due to the incident on the street. There was something deeper. *O, Mr. Brame,* he thought. *I doubt if you know my Saviour. Somehow I must arrange for you to meet Him.*

There seemed small hope of this, however, as the weeks and months went by. To be sure, the Pastor frequently saw the big policeman on the street. From time to time he even offered a friendly advance, hoping to find a chink in the armor of toughness that covered every part of the makeup of this arm of the law. But to no avail. The more he saw, the more the Pastor was convinced that Brame had never known the Lord. On more than one occasion he watched him as he leaped from the curb toward some oncoming driver who in his opinion was exceeding the speed limit. His whistle would blast, his arms would start waving, his face would grow almost purple with rage as he flagged down the suspected speeder. What usually followed was the same kind of scornful blast that had been delivered in front of the post office on that other morning.

Each time he was rebuffed personally, or saw the bitter rebuke administered by the policeman to others, the Pastor said in his heart, *O, my friend, if you only knew my Saviour! And someday, God willing, I will introduce you to Him.*

Busy, crowded days sped past. The delightful days of spring gave way to the lush and golden days of summer. The blue grass robing the hills took on darker hues as the summer sun beat down.

Often at the close of the day, the Pastor climbed to the summit of one of the hills surrounding his home and sat quietly in the twilight. These were the favorite hours. In every direction, as far as the eye could see, the rolling earth stretched itself in graceful folds. It was as though the hand of God had chosen this land to experiment in creating beauty. Here He made a hill with a pointed dome rising sharp and clean; there He put a graceful mound, soft and curving like the sand castles children build. Over there another like the round face of a baby. And then He sprinkled over it all the seed of the blue grass and put into the seed a tenacity and an urgency that gave it power to defy the plow and the erosion of the storms. Then He added to it a lovely greenness that made it look like rich velvet.

On a hundred slopes the red Herefords grazed and the herds of black Angus bent their heads to the succulent grass. No wonder the Pastor loved these hours when he feasted his eyes and his soul on the panorama of beauty so lavishly spread beneath him and around him. At such times he felt the closeness of God, and imagined that what he felt in his soul was akin to the joyous anticipation of Adam as in the cool of the day he listened for the footfalls of his Maker in the garden

18

of the Lord.

It was in such a twilight hour one day that the Pastor poured out his heart, interceding for the policeman. By now to win this man to Christ had become almost a passion burning deep in his soul. From time to time he asked himself why this man more than others called up a chord of love and compassion from the depths of his being. Could it be that the desire to bring him to Christ was a subtle form of revenge? Did it go back to that day when he had been stung by the caustic words on the main street? Was this some way of saying, "Mister, I'll show you"?

With such disturbing thoughts the Pastor wrestled until he felt certain his intentions had been purged of all that was unworthy. This only left him with a deeper concern and firmer determination that a case-hardened cop was going to meet Jesus. So as he sat leaning against a boulder on the top of his favorite hill, the minister poured out his heart in prayer.

"Lord God," he prayed, "open a door to that stubborn heart. Surely, Lord, he needs Thee. Thou seest the bitterness and gall that curdles his very soul. Please, God, show me some way to reach him."

Much of his prayer that day was too deep to put into words. It was a soul hungering for another soul. It was a yearning — reaching pleading hands to heaven. It was long, deep thoughts groping to find a way through the maze of a lost sinner's stubborn rejection of all that pertained to God.

As the darkness fell, the Pastor returned with heavy steps to his home. That was the night the telephone rang and the door for which he had prayed was opened. It was a desperate voice that spoke through the telephone receiver. The nervous quavering and the high, almost hysterical pitch indicated that its owner was clinging to the thin edge of self-control by sheer determination.

"Pastor," the voice spoke, "I need help. I've come to the end of the road. I am not a member of your church, I belong

19

to another church in the city, but my minister is away, and this cannot wait until he returns.''

''Who are you?'' the Pastor interrupted. ''I will be glad to help you if I can, but I would like to know first of all to whom I am speaking.''

''I beg your pardon,'' came the quick reply. ''I am so distraught, I forgot to tell you.''

The Pastor's heart leaped when the voice continued, ''I am Mrs. Brame. My husband is on the police force. Perhaps you know him, or at least have seen him around town.''

Smiling to himself, the Pastor answered, ''Yes, Ma'am, I seem to recall an occasion when I met your husband.''

''I cannot stand it any more,'' the thin voice sobbed into the phone. ''Please help me. Help my husband. Our marriage is breaking up. We can't go on like this.''

Quickly the Pastor suggested that they might discuss the matter better in her home. She agreed, saying it was convenient for him to meet with her even then.

The story she told was not a pleasant one. She revealed how the years had changed her husband.

''Oh, he was so different at one time,'' she said — ''considerate, kind and courteous. Everyone liked him instinctively. But I have watched him lose all of these fine qualities. I have watched him lose his friends. All of this has affected our marriage, and I have watched him become like a stranger even to me. ''

The Pastor listened closely, hoping to discover somewhere a clue, a key that would unlock the stubborn heart of the man he longed to see become a Christian. From time to time he raised questions that might be indicative of a possibility, but the man remained an enigma until —

''You know,'' Mrs. Brame said half to herself, ''it has almost reached the point where he has to go fishing alone.''

''Does he like to fish?'' the Pastor inquired eagerly.

''Oh, yes, he goes every time he gets a chance; many times

all alone.''

"That's it, Mrs. Brame. I believe that is the way I can reach him. Any fisherman in the world will talk about fishing. Your husband may not know it, but I am going fishing for him, and I will dangle some attractive bait under his nose the first chance I get.''

A look of relief lighted the woman's anxious face. "Oh, I hope you can get to know him. I believe if he knew you, or anyone who would try to befriend him and help him it might make a difference.''

For a moment there was a faraway look in the Pastor's eyes. When he spoke, his voice was vibrant with confidence. "Mrs. Brame, getting to know me would make small difference in your husband. I want him to get to know my Lord. He will do the changing. But I need your help. Do you believe that God really answers prayer?''

"Beyond any question I do," came the fervent reply. "I feel in my heart that talking to you tonight is an answer to the deepest prayers of my soul.'' Her lips began to quiver and the tears slipped down her face, The words came in sobs. "I have prayed — oh, how I have prayed for him!''

Knowing within himself how a heart can yearn and how difficult it was to watch and *wait* in prayer, the Pastor spoke with tenderness.

"I know. And God knows. You pray with me. Tonight, if you are willing, let's make a covenant to ask God daily to open a way to your man's heart.''

As she dried the tears from her eyes, the Pastor said, "Now let me talk to you. Mrs. Brame, tonight I ask you to put your burden in God's hands and leave it there. You are breaking yourself to pieces with concern. I can see why you are. If I were in your place, I would probably do the same thing. However, you don't have to carry this burden.''

Seeing that his listener was about to object, he headed her off saying, "Oh, I know you will continue to desire this thing

21

above all else and I am not going to be so foolish as to suggest that all of the concern will leave your heart. Yet, it is possible to have a quiet, sure confidence that will take the burden out of it and bring peace to your heart. Mrs. Brame, why not try trusting in God? You have said you believe He answers prayer. You know, of course, that He has promised to hear and to heed and to answer. God loves you, Mrs. Brame, He loves you. Try leaning on the everlasting arms that He has promised are underneath always.''·

The protest could be constrained no longer. ''Oh, I *do* trust Him. I pray constantly, Pastor — you just don't have any idea of how much I do believe.''

''But do you *trust* Him?'' The Pastor looked deep into her eyes as he asked the question. ''If you do, you will leave this whole matter in His hands. Let us suggest this — pray once more. Tonight when you are quiet, go aside somewhere alone. Then put your husband in God's hands. Tell Him you are turning this desire and concern over to Him. Say to Him, 'Lord God, I know I cannot; I have tried all I know to do. Now, with all my heart, I give Thee my burden, my concern, my need. Lord God, my husband's salvation is in Thy hands.'

''I can assure you there will come a quietness and a confidence that will fill your soul. When you have committed yourself and your loved one to Him, if disturbing thoughts should come, or questions and doubts arise, as well they might, you can say to your heart, 'But that is not my problem now. I have given that to God.' ''

Receiving assurance that his advice would be followed that very night, the Pastor departed.

The next day, as the Pastor drove along Main Street, sure enough, there was the big policeman. He was leaning against the wall of a department store building watching the flow of traffic. The minister parked, making sure that he deposited a nickel in the meter before making his way toward the corner where the officer stood. ''Old boy,'' he chuckled to himself, "this is one day I *don't* want to be blessed out."

Trying to appear casual, even though every heartbeat was a prayer, he strolled up to the policeman.

"Hello there," he said.

With a barely audible grunt, and with scarcely a glance, the policeman indicated that he was aware of the minister's presence.

It would take more than a cold rebuff to turn the Pastor aside from his purpose now. He knew a way he could arouse more than cold hostility.

"Say, I've heard you are quite a fisherman." Now the cold stare was lingering a little longer.

"Yeah?"

"Uh huh. They tell me you fish a lot and much of the time you go alone. Now, Mr. Brame, I know a lot of men who go fishing, and I have long since learned that when a fellow fishes alone, it's usually because he has some favorite spots that he knows he can catch fish and he isn't about to tell anyone where they are. If I were to ask you where you go, you would give me some vague answer that would reveal exactly nothing. So I am going to be presumptuous to the point of asking you to let me go with you. I promise you that I will guard your favorite fishing hole as a secret. The fact of the matter is, I haven't had time to locate the good fishing waters, and I don't have time to go fishing often. So when I go, I want to bring home something worthwhile."

For a moment a look of lively interest appeared on the officer's countenance, but quickly the distrust came back.

The Pastor's heart sank and he all but groaned aloud in disappointment as the only comment was, "Maybe we can get together sometime." And with that the officer moved on up the street.

That seemed to end the matter. On other occasions the minister sought to bring up the subject again, but always there was that look which said, *Move along, Preacher*. Still

23

he did not abandon his efforts. The summer slipped away, and the glorious fall moved quickly in to occupy its place. On every hand there was beauty such as the Pastor had never seen. The maples, which grew in abundance, put on their fall fashion show. The oaks and poplars tried vainly to compete and then gave up in drab defeat. At last the maples, too, seemed to tire of their profuse splendor and disrobed for the long sleep of winter.

That winter was fierce. Sometimes the wind howled down the mountainsides and drove the temperature down and down until the very air seemed to crackle with brittleness. For days on end the leaden clouds swooped over the mountains and with seeming glee released their burden of snow. For weeks the only ground to be seen was where the bitter winds swept the earth bare. There were cozy days when the Pastor was snowbound with his family and there was the delight of popping corn and toasting marshmallows over the blue flame of the coal in the fireplace. There were nights which saw great bonfires at the top of some icy street and crowds of people, young and old, coasting downhill on sleds with breathless speed.

But never for a day did the Pastor forget his man. A cold day to him was "as cold as that cop's heart." Ice-covered steps were as slippery "as that policeman trying to avoid me."

Then at last it was spring again. Once more the earth seemed to leap with life. Scarcely had the last snow bank melted before the earth brought forth with a surge of delight. By far the best thing that came with spring was the surprise when one day Brame walked up to the Pastor and said, "Let's go fishing." Just like that, the weeks and months of hoping, praying, bore fruit.

Quickly the plans were made for the next day. Important appointments were cancelled, a crowded schedule was rearranged. "An emergency situation has arisen," the Pastor explained to those who had to be called. Under his breath he added, "I'm going fishing — for a man."

When he met Brame the next morning, however, he received another setback. Before entering the Pastor's car, the policeman stuck his head in at the window and said, "Listen, Preacher. This is a good day for fishing, but a mighty poor day for talking religion. Understand?"

The Pastor grinned sheepishly. "All right. Today we just fish."

The spot to which they drove, deep in the heart of the towering mountain range was a place of rare splendor. The earth was just beginning to open its treasure chest of emeralds and was busy hanging them on every tree branch and spilling them with lavish hands across the hills. And what made it complete was that the fish were biting that morning. By noon the two men had taken a string of beauties from the rushing torrent of the cold, clear mountain stream. At midday they found a glade in a grove of giant hemlocks and sat in the shade of a giant boulder to eat lunch. For the first time since the Pastor had known him, Brame seemed relaxed and at ease. Obviously the cool, cathedral-like glen, the happy bubbling of the stream, had mellowed him. This appeared to the Pastor the moment to speak of things that had long been on his heart.

"Surely a man can see the hand of God in a beautiful place like this," was his tentative beginning. Only silence met his overture.

"It must have been in a spot that looked like this that God and Adam walked and talked in the beginning," he continued. No comment. His companion sat immobile with closed eyes and chin on chest as though asleep.

Once more the Pastor tried. "You know, it just doesn't seem possible that a man could live in the midst of so much evidence of the presence of a Creator and close his mind and heart to all he sees and hears and smells and feels at a time like this."

With a disgusted grunt, Brame stood up, picked up his rod and started back toward the stream. "Save your sermon for Sunday, Reverend," he growled. "You're just wasting it on me." But the growl was not so fierce as before. The dismissal did not have the previous note of finality. The Pastor's heart sang within him. As he looked toward the receding figure of his companion, he said to himself, *My friend, maybe – just maybe – you felt His presence here, too. Maybe you heard His footsteps for a moment.*

From that day the policeman's attitude was different toward the minister. By degrees the icy indifference melted. On occasions he even crossed the street to pass a few words with the Pastor. Almost always now he waved whenever he spied the minister driving by. There were other days of companionship on the banks of streams and rivers. Line upon line, precept upon precept the Pastor spoke his simple witness of a loving God. And bit by bit it began to sink in. Like one coaxing a shy child or a creature of the wild, the Pastor offered his friendship and understanding. And once convinced that the friendship was genuine, Brame responded with ever-increasing heartiness.

Then one day the dam that had blocked his lonely heart for so long was broken down. The Pastor would never forget that day. Again they were fishing together. They sat contently by a stream that meandered through a meadow. The sun was obviously getting sleepy and would soon excuse itself behind the curtain of the horizon. The magic of the twilight was weaving its spell. In a nearby clump of alders, a wood thrush lifted its song like an impassioned flute. Swaying on a reed, a red-winged blackbird sounded its evening hymn of praise. From a distance the silver clanging of a cowbell reached through the quietness and touched them. Not many words were passing between the two fishermen as they sat and watched the floating corks on the surface of the stream.

26

Quite suddenly Brame spoke. "Pastor," he said, "we have been together often. I have heard what you said; I have watched you like a hawk."

His voice took on a pleading. "It is real, isn't it — this thing you have found? this closeness to God you seem to have and have mentioned so many times?"

The Pastor held his breath for fear of interrupting the musing thoughts that came with such strangeness from the lips of his friend.

"You know, Rev" — by now this word frequently took the place of the more formal *Reverend* – "I have seen so much meanness and corruption and evil in the years I have been a cop, I guess I have just about quit believing in anything or anybody. I see people do things in the dark that nobody would ever dream they could do — I mean so-called good people, respectable folks! I guess I concluded long ago that everything in this old world has got a rotten spot in it somewhere. And now I feel trapped by it all. Rev, do you reckon there is any hope for a fellow like me finding what you have and starting all over again?"

Before answering, awed by the opportunity before him, the Pastor whispered, "Lord Jesus, come and be with us now. My friend here will soon want to meet You."

Then came Jesus.

Some might say it was imagination, but the Pastor felt the familiar reassurance of the touch of an unseen hand upon his shoulder. In his soul the voice that spoke worlds into being said, "I am here."

Now he dared to speak. He said, "I reckon there is a mighty good chance that you will find what you are seeking if you will just understand and believe that it is not found in a *what,* but in a *who.*"

All the pent-up yearning in the heart of the man of God burst out. "Oh, Brame, I want you to know my Saviour. Once I needed Him and sought Him even as you do now.

27

That day something in me died and I was glad to see it go, because something wonderful came alive and took its place. Someone moved into my heart in that hour and He has never left it for a moment.

The big policeman had begun to weep softly. "How did you find Him, Rev?" he asked.

"I didn't find Him. He found me. All I did was to stop running away from Him. I just said, 'Lord, I'm lost, and I can't find my way any more. Let me take Your hand.' I didn't have to take His hand. He took hold of mine. I said, 'Lord, I've made a mess of things and I haven't got much to offer You, but such as I am, I would like for You to have me, if You will.' My soul was in the dust that day, and for awhile in His presence I felt like the lowest thing on earth. I don't know what He said or what He did, I only know that I felt like I had been born all over again."

The intensity on the tear-wet face before him was almost frightening. "Tell me, Rev. How can *I* find Him?"

"You don't have to find Him, my friend," the Pastor said. "He is already here. If you can say to Him from your heart something like I said to Him, if you will just give yourself to Him, you will find all you are looking for and a thousand times more."

"It has been a long time since I prayed, Rev."

"That's all right. He has *waited* for a long time for you to pray again. Forget I am here and settle it now."

For long minutes the only sound that interrupted the silence was the sobbing of a broken and contrite heart. But when that big policeman lifted his head and turned toward the Pastor, the radiance beaming in every line of his face made all the waiting, yearning and praying worthwhile.

There is one more thing you should know about this story. The next Monday morning the Pastor parked his car in a spot before the same post office. A booming voice hailed him. "Hey, Rev! Wait a minute." Big feet came pounding along the pavement, running. Sunrise was all over the ruddy face of the policeman as he stopped breathless before the minister.

"Rev, I did it. I went with my wife to her church and when the invitation was given He just took me by the hand and led me down that aisle."

Joyfully the Pastor threw his arms about the burly blue-clad shoulders. Those who passed by, no doubt, thought the two men pounding each other on the back had lost their minds. But, then, if those who passed by had looked again, they might have seen Jesus there in front of the post office with His arms around them both.

And so, friend, you may drive down that Main Street one of these days and if you go a little too fast you will probably hear a police whistle blast and you will see a big, red-faced policeman leap from the sidewalk, arms waving like a windmill. And your heart may nearly stop beating with apprehension — until you look into his eyes and see the soft light there and hear the voice that used to growl, quietly requesting that you take it easy. If this ever happens, just remember you have met the big, mean cop who met the great, wonderful Christ.

[1]Psalm 19:1

[2]Psalm 141:3

29

2

LIKE
PENTECOST

THAT MONDAY SEEMED a most unlikely time to have a Board meeting. It was Labor Day, the time when so many people are having their last opportunity for summer fun and pleasure. The Pastor did not expect that many members of the Board would be in town to attend the meeting, but it was the regularly scheduled meeting date and as far as he knew there was nothing particularly urgent to be considered. Therefore if the attendance was off, it would not matter too greatly.

So it was that he headed for the church with the expectation of sitting through another of the endless meetings pertinent to the program of a wide-awake, thriving church.

It was a golden hour. This September day had been one of unusually rare beauty. The sun had beat down with the intense burning common to late summer days, as though it realized that there was little time to ripen the harvest and wrap the earth in a warm golden blanket before the lazy dropping of autumn leaves and the deceptive breath of the autumn breezes brought the drowsy lull that precedes the

30

long cold sleep of winter.

Already the maple leaves had begun to deck themselves out for their spectacular masquerade ball. While the maples were busy putting on their gaudiest, brightest colors, the stately gums presented themselves in garments of deep rich red, like the fire in the heart of a ruby. The poplars and the elms brought out the yellow garb that they admired so much they never changed the shade of color. Even the mighty oaks, so loftily dignified and through dignity so reluctant to make a spectacle of themselves, put on a bit of flaming rouge. The towering pines and hemlocks lifted their heads in disdain and agreed among themselves just to wear their usual dark green velvets, although they did condescend to brush off a few of their tags that were becoming a bit frayed from summer wear.

The twilight was gathering the purple folds of its long flowing robes about the sleepy creatures of the earth. With defiance other creatures were crying to the sun to stay its downward plunge and to hold back the encircling veil of the night. A nighthawk screeched its protest at the waning day, a cricket chirped its greeting to familiar shadows. All this the Pastor noticed with glad and grateful heart as he walked toward his church.

Waiting on the steps to meet him was Alan Rutherford, secretary of the Board and executive vice-president of one of the banks in the city.

"Hi, Pastor," he called a cheery greeting.

"Hello, Alan. How are things with you?" the Pastor replied.

Rutherford continued, "I guess we will be off in the attendance tonight. We may not have a quorum, but in any case I have a matter I would like to bring up."

"Sure, Alan," the Pastor readily agreed. "I don't think there is much business to come up tonight, so there should be plenty of time to consider any matter you wish to present."

The secretary said, "This is not a matter of business really.

31

It is just something I have had on my heart for a good while, something that I use at the bank."

The Pastor wondered what the banker had in mind to discuss. Whatever it was, whether it was financial or otherwise, it would be worth hearing. His gaze lingered on the tall, slightly stooped figure of the banker. His face was craggy, deeply lined under a shock of snow-white hair. The nose was large and prominent, and Alan was given to pulling at it with a cupped hand whenever he was agitated or in deep thought. The wide-spaced deep-set eyes were a startling blue and bright as a child's. Seldom did a twinkle leave them for long. The wide, mobile mouth was a trifle too large, but the jutting chin gave a quality of strength to the whole, attractive face.

Here is a man, the Pastor mused, as he looked at his companion, *who has learned much from the wise teacher named Experience, and he has been an apt pupil.* Still, he wondered what Rutherford had on his mind, but he refrained from asking since he was not to moderate the meeting anyway.

One by one other members gathered until a majority of them were on hand. The meeting proceeded in the usual fashion and all of the matters of business were quickly dispensed with. The chairman, John Newland, asked for any other matters to be presented before adjournment.

It was then that Alan Rutherford stood slowly to his feet. "Mr. Chairman," He said, "I have something I would like to talk about for a few minutes if you do not mind and if these men are not in a hurry to adjourn the meeting."

The chairman nodded to indicate that Rutherford had the floor. The quiet deep voice of the banker began.

"Brethren, this is something I have considered bringing up for a good while, but I have hesitated to do so. Usually we have a lot of business to dispose of in our meetings and I have not thought it wise to prolong them. Besides, I am not very good at making speeches and I guess that is what this will

32

become before I am finished.''

He paused momentarily as though to make sure the other men were willing for him to proceed. Seeing no indication of unrest or dissatisfaction, he resumed.

"Brethren, I have two offices at the bank for my personal use. One is the outer office where many of you have been. It is the place where I have interviews and meetings and conduct the routines of my job. Most of you do not know that I have another office. It is much smaller, and it has no furnishings except a straight chair, a small table and a card file. It is in this second office that I conduct my spiritual business. I head for that little room before the bank opens for business and there seek the presence of my Senior Director. I read His Word so that I might have wisdom and guidance for the day. Then I just talk things over with Him, and especially do I talk to Him about the information contained in that card file. There are some two hundred cards in the file, brethren, and on each card a name and some information that tells me about that particular individual's personal needs.

"You see, they are the names of people who have come to me for advice and help. Usually their request takes the form of asking for counseling or help concerning financial matters. In many cases that is their real problem and we discuss it from that angle alone. However, across the years I have come to know that many times a surface problem is only the outward indication of a deeper one; that so often the material problems grow out of a basic spiritual problem. By asking leading questions tactfully, I am often able to get them to reveal and discuss the deeper needs.

"Now I do not keep that file just to have records on hand. Those names, more than two hundred of them, are my prayer list for each day. Some time during the day I call all of those names at the throne of God and ask Him to help them and to enable me to help them, if that is His will.''

The old man's rugged face took on a shy, half-fearful look.

Such was his humility that he seemed to weigh the question of continuing so much information about himself. Perhaps if his concern had not been so deep and the compassion in his heart had been less a drive within, he might have decided to stop at that point. As it was, he was compelled to go on even at the risk of what seemed to him to be putting himself in the limelight. So his rich voice spoke again.

"Brethren, the thing that really concerns me is that those two hundred people who have confided with me some of their spiritual needs are just a minute portion of the great mass of people in our city who need the Lord. And we know that. We know these people who desperately, hungrily need Christ are round about us on every side. Here our church stands, supposedly to be a lighthouse unto these people in moral and spiritual darkness.

"Maybe it is a lighthouse, but is the light bright enough to be seen by those out there for whom the darkness is a deep and ofttimes terrible thing? Jesus said something about a man not putting his candle under a bushel. I think our churches have sometimes committed that tragic error. Perhaps our church has, too. I know this, that none of that group of two hundred people I pray for every day are coming to this church, and few of them are worshiping in any church. And yet I am persuaded their basic need is the need of Christ.

"Why haven't they found Him, brethren? Have any of us personally bothered to tell them about Him? I have not. I have given them sound spiritual counsel. I have suggested that they pray about their problems and needs, but they don't know how to pray or else they tried prayer, and not understanding how God answers, they got disgusted and gave it up. I have even quoted some Scripture now and then. But frankly, unless I was put on the spot by some question or comment, I did not tell them about my Saviour.

"This disturbs me deeply, gentlemen, for I call myself a Christian. I tell myself and I tell the Lord that I love Him. But do I really love Him when each day my life touches the lives of people who need Him more than anything on this earth and I am strangely given to gab about everything else and strangely tongue-tied about Jesus?''

A look of deep sadness and painful self-reproach appeared on the deeply lined, gentle old face. This public self-examination was not pleasant. Again Alan Rutherford looked at the faces before him, one by one. Whatever he saw there reassured him that they felt no reproach for his words. He passed a thin, blue veined hand along the length of his prominent nose, a token of the deep concern that troubled him. Then he proceeded.

"The thing of it is, brethren, I *know* they need Christ. I *know* He is the answer for them. But for some reason I seldom get quite to the point of introducing them to my Lord."

His glowing eyes swept over the Board members who sat silent and still before him.

"Am I alone in this failure?" he asked. "I wonder how many of you men use your opportunities to speak of Jesus to the hungry hearts that are seeking Him as they come to us. Here you are doctors, lawyers, insurance men, storekeepers. There is not a one of us who does not daily meet people who need Christ. All of us have folks tell us their problems, share with us their burdens, reveal to us their heartaches. And every one of us comes here on Sunday supposedly to worship the Lord and to find guidance and strength for His service. In what service does He expect us to use the guidance and strength He gives us? Just in the making of money for ourselves, in running an honest business, in dealing truthfully and justly with our fellow men? Is that the service we are supposed to render for Him between Sundays? If it is, then either we have a mighty little Christ or else we have a great Christ of whom we have a mighty little understanding."

35

Rutherford's sad face now took on an expression of deep concern as he hurried on. "I do not reproach you men. If what I am saying points to guilt, then I am the guiltiest of all because my own heart reproves me of my failure and I stand condemned at the tribunal of my own conscience. However, I am concerned about this matter, deeply concerned."

The tears started to glide down the wrinkles in his face. The great old heart was spilling over as he concluded. "It is just that there are so many people who need *Him,* and many of us who profess to know Him best and love Him the most are personally doing so little about it."

Almost apologetically the old man finished his speech and slowly walked to his seat. A gripping silence followed his words. For a long minute there was not even a sigh or a movement. The chairman of the Board, at a loss for words, arose and commented, "Well, I guess it is time to go home."

No one moved. No one made the usual motion to adjourn. The almost tangible silence continued. The Pastor knew that this was a moment of deep significance, that souls were being searched by ruthless self-examination. Quite suddenly someone, the Pastor could never recall who it was, spoke reluctantly. "Mr. Chairman, I think it is time for us to linger here for prayer instead of going home. I cannot speak for others, but I know I need to get on my knees and ask my Lord to forgive me."

A soft sob came from somewhere among the group. Another voice, muffled and heavy with emotion said, "That's the way I feel, too."

The Pastor, sensing that something tremendous was in the balances, spoke with a hush. "Brethren, I suppose we all feel the same. I would like to kneel here and get some things straight with my Lord. Perhaps you would like to join me."

The suggestion was all that it took. Almost as one man, the members of the Board slipped out of their seats onto their knees. It began quietly enough, but something caught fire.

Suddenly the room was electrified. The Pastor could actually feel the hair prickle on his head. As it caught the kneeling men in its embrace, an audible gasp went up from them. There could be but one explanation. *Then came Jesus.* He moved silently among those men, His hand was placed on each of them in turn. They began to pray aloud. They sobbed, they wept. They poured out their shame for their failures. They yearned for forgiveness. They yielded themselves anew. They prayed themselves full of His love and power.

Even after all the prayers were done and silence had come again to the room, the vibrant Presence remained holding the men captive and spellbound in the agonizingly sweet joy of the experience that had shaken them and filled them to the deepest recesses of their souls.

When at last the spell was broken, the rapturous faces of the group glistened with something beside the wetness of their tears. Every countenance was touched with awe, by expressions of bewilderment. But one and all, on those faces still lingered a beauty and purity that was the afterglow of glory.

The chairman brushed at his eyes as though he were just awakening, and spoke for them all. ''I cannot explain what I felt or what happened here tonight, but I can tell the world it was the most wonderful thing that ever happened to me.''

The next Sunday was one of the high points in all the Pastor's ministry. As he ended his sermon and gave the invitation for people to come to Christ, spontaneously, with no word of encouragement or appeal from him, the members of the Board came from every part of the congregation. One by one they gripped the Pastor's hand and said things like, ''I want to give my life anew in the service of Christ. I want to make my witness count for Jesus. I want Him to have all of me.''

It is small wonder that the church was soon aflame with a renewed spirit of dedication. None of those men ever wasted a moment wondering, as others wondered, what had stirred and lifted and filled the church so that streams of people came into it until it doubled and tripled its membership. They knew the reason. They had been there when Jesus came.

3

THE LONELY
MOUNTAIN CABIN

Wearily the Pastor plodded his way along the tortured winding of the footpath up the hollow. It was choked with rocks. In places shale had broken loose from the overhanging ledges and had fallen to the path below, making the footing treacherous. The hollow itself was almost like a tunnel. Across the years, cascading torrents of rain had cut a gash in the face of the mountain like a deep furrow plowed by a drunken giant; it wandered in and out among the cliffs and outcroppings of granite. In places it was but a narrow ravine with walls that almost met above. In spots the sides sloped more gently and the hollow was wider, smoother.

In the gloom of the evening, the ravine was dark, and the Pastor's feet stumbled over unseen rocks. His progress was made even more difficult by the blast of the cold wind that moaned down the hollow. It was not the lateness of the hour, however, that made the man hurry as best he could along the difficult course. Somewhere up there ahead of him, how far he did not know, a man was dying; the dying man had sent for a preacher.

Into such places as this the Pastor had gone many times in response to human need. Word would come to him from some of his church members or from some other source that there was someone back in the hills or hollows, far removed from highways and towns, accessible only by walking such forsaken and winding paths as the one along which he pushed upward now, who needed Jesus and who wanted a preacher to show the way to find Him. Sometimes these paths ended at lonely cabins, nestling in remote clearings. Occasionally the Pastor was surprised to discover a dozen or more homes clustered at the head of a hollow — family clans living there isolated from society and rarely leaving the fortress of the mountains. People like these seldom if ever entered a church, and few of them knew any minister personally.

All of this mattered not at all to the Pastor. It took no more than the knowledge that someone, somewhere, among these hollows and hills needed his Saviour to make him put aside the demands of a busy city pastorate and set him climbing, sweating, panting his way up some boulder-strewn pathway. Gradually word of his willingness to come and minister had spread in these remote places until the calls came frequently, and he had begun to feel an ever-deepening desire to build a chapel for these people to worship in, a burden for someone to live among them and preach the unsearchable riches of Christ.

So a lovely little chapel had been erected and since there was no one else to do it, the Pastor found himself giving Sunday afternoons to preaching there. The people had come, not many at first and those who had come were withdrawn and suspicious. For a while only the women and children would enter the chapel to worship. The men, clad in blue bibbed overalls remained outside, sitting under the trees and whittling or talking softly while the services went on within. It was a glad day for the Pastor when he began to see the suspicion of his mountain flock turning gradually to warm acceptance, then to enthusiastic response, and the little church become crowded Sunday after Sunday with *men* as well as women and children. Thus it was that he had grown familiar with most of the paths that led to the homes of these mountain people.

However, the path he traveled now was strange to him. He had never seen or even heard of the man whose cabin he was seeking in the gathering darkness until someone had called and said, "Old Painter is dying. He wants you to come."

It was almost fully dark when he reached the point where the ravine widened out into a bowl-shaped clearing. The wind had not lessened with the lowering of the sun. Its icy fingers reached inside the heavy coat the Pastor wore and seemed to pinch his flesh. The wind roared through the bare trees that covered the face of the mountain, standing like black stubble on the steep slopes. The trees protested the icy embrace of the gale, rattling their limbs in rage and defiance at being denied at least the quiet and calm of night. The light that spilled out of the windows from the glowing lamps in the cabin caused the warmth of gratitude to spread through the minister's tired body and lent new strength to his stumbling feet.

No sooner had the Pastor moved into the clearing than the long baying of a hound dog announced his presence. Still some distance from the cabin silhouetted against the darkness of the mountain by the last lingering light of day, the Pastor stood still. He knew from experience that the moment the dog had begun to cry the presence of an intruder, every occupant of the house had become alert, suspicious, and that even now searching eyes were glued to some crack seeking the identity of the newcomer.

It was understood among these mountaineers that no stranger was allowed to walk boldly to the house without first making his presence and his business known. There were

41

many tales circulating among the hills of people who had been shot when they moved too quickly or too quietly about the premises of some of the hill folk.

Perhaps their native suspicion of strangers went back to days when marauding Indians were the scourge of these secluded cabins, some of which had housed generation after generation and in which the tales of bloody raids were a part of family history and heritage. Some of it, no doubt, was the result of the solitary life these people lived, a life which seldom took them further than the next valley or across the mountain range into hidden hollows where friends and relatives dwelled. Perhaps in part that suspicion was a carry-over from the not-too-distant time when in many of these out-of-the-way places moonshine whisky was manufactured. In any case, the Pastor knew his environment well enough to know that it would be wise to conform to custom and wait until he was invited to approach nearer.

He shivered as he stood there in the faint light. The cold was now so intense that the moisture of his breath froze and made his nostrils pinch together with every breath. For a long minute he waited.

Then from the darkness of the front porch of the cabin a voice called, "Who is it?"

Over the blast of the wind the Pastor shouted back, "I am the pastor Mr. Painter sent for. I would like to see him if I may."

There was the sound of subdued murmurings as the voice spoke to someone inside the house. Then aloud came the invitation, "Preacher, you can come on up."

The words were a welcome sound. Not only did they indicate that he was known and had been accepted, but also they opened the way to deliverance from the cold and to blessed warmth within, for the wind was laden with the spicy pungent fragrance of wood smoke. As he drew near to the cabin, the Pastor became aware of its smallness. He estimated that it could not consist of but two or at most three small rooms. How many people lived in this space he did not know, but he had been in places no larger than this where as many as a dozen people in a family lived. Sometimes when the hills were gripped by the cold such as on this night, dogs and calves and chickens and even small pigs were crowded in with the human occupants. More than once, pigs had been chased out when the Pastor entered or chickens had been shoved from crude chairbacks so he could have a seat.

This sort of thing no longer startled or dismayed him. He had come to expect and accept it as a part of the pattern of life among people for whom a living came hard, because it had to be carved out of the rugged, reluctant steeps of the mountains that gave up blessings only begrudgingly. A few scrawny chickens, a pig or two constituted a winter's supply of meat for these people who tilled the rocky slopes or worked a few days seasonally for almost nothing on the bigger farms in the valley. So he had come to expect crude and humble houses whenever he climbed the paths that led to mountain homes. But they were homes, and he was welcome among them.

More than once, when he had ministered in some time of sorrow or trouble in such a place, he had been "paid" by being given a chicken or a ham. A few times, at first, he had made the mistake of refusing, or even worse of offering to pay for the gift, but soon he had learned from the looks of wounded pride, or even of outraged disappointment, that he had unknowingly administered an insult. Thus he had come to accept such expressions of friendship and gratitude. But many times he would later eat the chicken or the ham and almost choke as he thought of the empty place the gift had created in the larder of the family that had bestowed it.

As he stepped onto the board porch of the simple home, he became aware of the fact that this cabin was even cruder than most. In the light that streamed through the one window in the front, he saw the rough boards from which the cabin was built. The boards had been nailed side by side vertically. Over the cracks thin strips had been nailed. He could not see the features of the dark figure that loomed near the doorway, but a deep, friendly voice greeted him with, "H'it's a cold night, h'ain't it, Preacher?"

"It surely is," the Pastor responded, extending his hand. The hand was engulfed in one much larger and rougher than his own. The strength with which it was gripped was almost cruel. He followed his guest into the cabin, both of them stooping as they passed through the low door, and stepped into a room made golden by lamplight and warm by a small iron stove that glowed cherry red. The rough, splintery boards of the floor were bare but pale with many scrubbings with lye soap. The walls of the small room were unlined. Fastened to one of the studs along the wall was a brightly colored calendar. Knot holes in the undressed boards that formed the walls had been plugged by paper or rags. There were two small windows in the room. In one of them rags had been stuffed where a pane of glass was broken. The rags danced merrily to the music of the wind that poured around them. There was no ceiling except the rafters and underside of the roof boards, blackened now by the smoke from many fires made in the iron stove. A handmade table, with no cloth to cover it, three rickety chairs, the iron stove and dimly seen bed in the shadowy corner of the room were the only furnishings.

With a quick glance, the Pastor took all this in and turned to look upon the man who had ushered him into the cabin. He saw a rugged, powerfully built man. The face behind a stubble of dark beard was deeply tanned by sun and wind. The features, stiff with embarrassment caused by the presence of a stranger, especially a stranger who was a minister, were craggy and sharply outlined. The deep blue eyes were piercing and glinted with shy friendliness. The man was dressed in a blue wool shirt, opened at the neck and with sleeves rolled up on muscular arms in spite of the cold that penetrated even within the room He wore brown corduroy pants and on his feet were heavy cowhide boots.

Sensing the Pastor's gaze upon him, the man looked up, a grin splitting the rugged, not unattractive face. Again the deep voice spoke. "Preacher, I'm Si Painter. I been here a few weeks looking after my pa, ever since he took worse and couldn't do for hisself."

He spoke with the slow drawl so common to mountain people. "I live acrost the ridge with my own family. Pa here's been living by hisself ever since Ma died eight years ago. He made out all right livin' here alone until a few weeks ago. He took sick then, and he has gone down steadily ever since. We had the doctor to him a couple of times. The doc said h'it's consumption, and there h'ain't nothin' kin be done for him."

The twangy drawl stopped for a moment, then resumed more softly. "I'm afeered he's dying, Preacher. He don't know anybody much for the last day or so, and he's been askin' for a preacher. That's why I sent word down the holler today askin' you to come. We ain't never been to yore chapel in the valley, but we heerd of you, that you go among us mountain people whenever you are ast to."

The Pastor listened attentively while the man spoke. Then he commented, "Mr. Painter, if your father is as ill as you say, wouldn't it have been better to call the doctor again, as well as a minister, or better still, shouldn't he be taken to a hospital?"

"No, Preacher, you don't know Pa," Si Painter answered emphatically. "I told him to let me get the doc back again, but he wouldn't hear to it, said he was goin' to die anyway and all he wanted was a preacher to come. And he shorely wouldn't hear of it to leavin' here to go to no hospital. Besides, I reckon you kin help him more than anybody else now."

45

At this moment a weak voice called from the bed in the corner, "Who is it, Si?"

"H'it's the preacher, Pa," Si replied to his father. "We done got word to him like you ast, and he just got here."

"Bring him over here, Son." The quavery voice spoke scarcely above a whisper. A spasm of coughing cut it off before it could speak further.

The Pastor moved quickly to .the bedside, pulling up a chair and seating himself in it. The gray, sickly face before him was almost ghostly. The skin was drawn so tightly across the bone structure it looked like wax. The eyes were deep pockets of exhausted suffering. On each cheek was the telltale pink glow. The siege of coughing gradually subsided leaving the slight form shaking upon the bed. The breathing was shallow and gasping now.

The Pastor reached out and took the thin, feverish hand of the dying man. Gently he stroked it while the shaking grew quieter and the breathing resumed the normal gasping of one dying of tuberculosis.

"Mr. Painter, if you do not feel able to talk, just let me talk. I think I know what you need and want to hear now. You don't have to say anything."

There was an impatient shaking of the gaunt and ghostly face. With a wheezing voice the old man answered, "Preacher, I h'ain't got long to talk and they h'ain't many words left in me. But I gotta say 'em whilst I can."

"All right, then," the Pastor reassured him. "You say whatever is on your heart. I will listen. But when you get tired, quit and let me talk awhile."

For a moment the thin blue lips of the sick man twitched with emotion. Two tears were squeezed from the tightly shut eyes and trickled down his face.

"Preacher," the gasping voice said, "I h'ain't been no church-goin' man in all my life. We h'ain't had no church to go to 'til you come to these parts. But I cain't offer that as no

46

excuse — I wouldn't of went if h'it had been there all the time. My pa before me was a godless man. My ma was a religious woman, and she tried to read us from the Bible and talk to us about God. But Pa used to make her hush and sometimes he flew into such a rage and threatened to beat her and burn the Bible, 'til she finally gave up tryin'.

"I was raised godless, Preacher, and I been godless all my life. I done a lot of wrong in my time. I broke all the laws in the book, I reckon, at one time or 'nother. Mostly I made moonshine whisky. Course, I say 'tain't wrong for a man to make whisky. The corn was mine and I figure 'twas up to me to decide if I ate h'it off'n a cob or drank h'it out of a bottle. But the law says 'twas wrong, so I am guilty.

"That h'ain't all. I done stole, I done drunk barrels of whisky. I done lied and cheated and maybe oncet I killed a man. At least he died a few weeks after I beat him."

The sick voice trailed away to a whisper. A sob shook the wasted form upon the bed. The Pastor thought the talk was ended, but from somewhere the old man drew up more strength and continued.

"All of my life until now I done denied God. Si there will bear me witness that many was the time I said to him and the other children, 'They h'ain't no God. A man has got to go h'it by hisself, make his own way. He don't need no god to tote him along.' "

The waxy face turned for a moment to where Si Painter stood silent, unmoving, as though seeking confirmation of his declaration. Then he turned his feverish eyes to the Pastor.

"I denied Him. I cursed His name. I broke His laws. I done Him wrong in every way. And now I know I got to go meet Him. And I'm scared, Preacher. I'm afeered to die."

He was openly weeping now. The Pastor's grip on the thin, hot hand was reassuring and from it came the self-control to resume.

"Preacher, they is a God, h'ain't they?"

With terrible earnestness the hollow eyes were burning into the Pastor's. The minister answered simply, "There is a God, Mr. Painter."

There was a cry in the next question, "Well, do you know Him, Preacher?"

"Yes, sir, I know Him. I have known Him for a long time."

"Then, tell me — what's He like, Preacher? I got to meet Him soon. I want to know what He's like."

For a moment the Pastor wondered how he could find the words to speak of the Infinite to this simple, ignorant mountaineer who had all of his life closed his mind to thoughts of God, his heart to feelings about Him, and who now in the eleventh hour yearned to know Him. Silently he prayed as at so many other times, "O, Lord, come to me now. Speak through my lips what needs to be said. Come Thyself to the bedside of this dying man who needs Thee and wants Thee, Saviour."

The feeling that surged through his entire being was the deep stirring of a Presence. His Lord had heard, had answered, was instantly, fully, radiantly there. Now, the Pastor knew, the words would flow, for they would not be his words. He would be only the instrument through which they sounded.

And the words came. They flowed. They reached out to a yearning heart. They conquered.

"Mr. Painter," the Pastor began. "Men have been asking that question almost from the beginning of time. Even those who believed there was a God, realized that they knew Him imperfectly, slightly, and wondered what He was like. There were those who looked at His works and said within their minds and hearts, 'Surely Someone designed and created and keeps all of this I see, but what is that Someone like?'

"Others like yourself marked Him off entirely, scoffed at

the idea of there being a God until in some moment of desperation like yours they came to see they had only fooled themselves; that there is a God with whom we all have to do. So your question is as old as time and as wide as the world.

"Thank God, Mr. Painter, there came a time when God gave the answer to that question. He gave it in a way that the simplest, most unlearned person on this earth could understand it. He gave that answer in a life that was lived out in this world for all to behold. The answer to your question and to the question of all men about God was given, is given, in Jesus Christ.

"I do not expect you to understand all the meaning of the Incarnation, the way God came in that life into this world to reveal Himself. I do not understand it all myself. No man can. It may help you, however, to liken it unto my presence here. You had heard of me before you sent for me today. But you did not know me. Others might have told you things about me — some true, some false, but you would have no way of being certain, because you had never met me. Then you asked for me to come to your home. My presence here tells you what you need to know. It is the visible presence of a Pastor, one whom you can see and touch and hear that tells you what I am like.

"So God came into this world, visibly, audibly. God came in a Presence, in a life, in a form that people could see and touch and hear. He showed the world in Christ what He is like. Whatever you or any person wants to know about God, you need but to look unto Christ Jesus. One among the followers of Christ asked about the same question you did. He said to the Lord, 'Show us the Father, and it sufficeth us.'[1] The answer Jesus gave him was, 'He that hath seen me hath seen the Father.'[2]

"That is how *your* question can be answered, my friend. I can tell you about Jesus and it is the same as telling you what God is like. Let me tell you some of it, Mr. Painter, some

49

things you need desperately to know now. I think that first of all and most of all you are anxious to know how God feels about you. That is your deepest concern, isn't it?''

The haggard face seemed too far spent even to change expression now, and there was not enough strength in the wasted form for even a nod of the head, but the feverish eyes burned with intensity, and the Pastor read in them the confirmation of the assumption.

"Mr. Painter," he continued gently, "in all fairness to you, I must say that all the wrongs and transgressions you have acknowledged have not gone unnoticed by your Maker. He is Holy. He is Just. He cannot ignore the breaking of His law any more than you could ignore the deliberate disobedience of your children when you had given them some command or some responsibility. But that's not all. God is love. And, my friend, I can say without one shadow of a doubt that God loves you.''

The old man was so startled by this affirmation that he choked again. The thin old body writhed beneath the covers as he fought for breath. When at last he had forced the coughing to cease by sheer determination, he held up his hand again to signify that he would speak.

For another long moment the words could not be forced out. Then he gasped, "Preacher, don't lie to me. Don't tell me such a thing if h'it h'ain't a fact. I've always been afeered of any God there might be, and I'm afeered of Him now. If what you say be the truth, then I don't need to fear Him no more.''

"I have told you nothing but the truth, Mr. Painter," the Pastor said with quiet earnestness. "I would not and could not deceive you now. There is no truth in all of this world more certain than the love of God. A hundred times and more Jesus spoke of it, revealed it, lived that love out before men. To a man named Nicodemus he said, 'For God so loved the world, that he gave his only begotten Son, that whosoever believeth in him should not perish, but have everlasting life.'[3]

"He spoke of it again when He gave a picture of what God is like in the parable we have come to call the story of the prodigal son. He told of a father who had two sons. One of them, the youngest, took everything his father gave him and ran away from home. He threw away every blessing he had. He wasted it all, until finally he got down on the same level with the swine he was hired to feed. Then one day he realized how foolish he was and said within his heart he would go home to his father and beg for the privilege of being even as much as a hired servant in his father's household.

"Oh, listen, my friend, to the words of Jesus.

> But when he was yet a great way off, his father saw him, and had compassion, and ran, and fell on his neck, and kissed him. And the son said unto him, Father, I have sinned against heaven, and in thy sight, and am no more worthy to be called thy son. But the father said to his servants, Bring forth the best robe, and put it on him; and put a ring on his hand, and shoes on his feet! And bring hither the fatted calf, and kill it; and let us eat, and be merry: for this my son was dead, and is alive again; he was lost, and is found.''[4]

The Pastor paused momentarily so the full force of the words could sink in. Then he spoke, "And that father, Mr. Painter, is a picture of God."

The old man groaned. His head rolled back and forth upon the pillow as though a physical agony twisted it. The thin, reedy voice sobbed, "And t'other one is a picture of me. O Preacher, he cain't love the likes of me. I done denied Him. I done shook my fist at the sky and cursed Him and dared Him to do anything about it." The words were punctuated by groans of anguish.

Si Painter, who had stood silently in the background during all of the converation now spoke softly. "Hush, Pa, you h'aint doin' yourself no good takin' on like this."

The old man made no reply. His head rolled back and forth, back and forth, as he wept uncontrollably.

"Mr. Painter," the Pastor said, "hear me again for a moment. Rather hear the words of Jesus. 'The publican, standing afar off, would not lift up so much as his eyes unto heaven, but smote his breast, saying, God be merciful to me a sinner.'[5] God heard that cry. God answered that prayer. When that man went to his home all the past was cleansed and forgiven. He had become a new person. It can happen to you, Mr. Painter."

"How? Oh, tell me how!" came the tortured cry.

"Do what the publican did, what the prodigal son did, what every poor sinner has to do, what I did, Mr. Painter. Just turn your heart to the Saviour. Tell him you have sinned. Ask Him to have mercy upon you and to forgive you. Tell Him that you give yourself into His hands now."

Scarcely had he completed the sentence when the words began to pour from the purplish lips. "Oh, Lord God, I done sinned. You know I done sinned terrible. They h'aint much I h'aint done, Lord. H'it don't rightly seem possible that you kin love the likes of me, but this preacher says you do and he tells me Jesus said you do. So h'it must be and I believe h'it, Lord." The voice had grown stronger with urgency. "Do you reckon you kin forgive me, Lord? Do you reckon you kin have mercy on a sinner like me?"

There was a sharp intake of breath as though a keen, cutting pain had knifed through him. But this time the gasp was not of illness; it was of wonder, astonishment, joy. A look of incredulity crept slowly over the parchment-like face. It began with a widening of the sunken eyes; they seemed to be set, staring at something so incredibly beautiful that it was unbelievable. It became a glowing softness; a radiance, like a light shining from within and working its way to the surface.

A glad cry struggled up from the deepest depths of his soul. "O Lord! O Lord!" It was the heralding of a birth. It was a hymn of praise and adoration. It was the echo of the joybells of heaven.

These were the last words the old man ever spoke in this world. The tired, sunken eyes closed wearily. The lines of fear were gone from the haggard face. Even the nearness of death did not stay the coming of an expression of unutterable contentment and peace from settling there.

Beside the bed the Pastor watched on through the interminable hours. Si Painter put wood in the stove and pulled a chair up to the rough table. He sat with his arms folded upon the table and his head upon his arms. Outside the wind howled and reached out fingers of cold to probe the cracks in the walls of the cabin. There were times during those long, lonely hours when the Pastor noticed that his trouser cuffs actually fluttered from the blasts of wind that came through the walls and windows.

Just before the first faint streak of light announced the approaching dawn, the thin body on the bed stirred faintly. There was a soft sigh of satisfaction. The Pastor looked and knew that it was the presence of Jesus that had etched the sweet, contented smile on the now dead face.

[1]John 14:8b

[2]John 14:9b

[3]John 3:16

[4]Luke 15:20-24

[5]Luke 18:13

4

INTO THE WILD
BLUE YONDER

PASTOR, ARE YOU going to fly to the convention?'' John Newland, the chairman of the Official Board, asked as they lingered over a cup of coffee and discussed plans for the trip the minister would take soon.

The Pastor rolled his eyes in make-believe horror and replied with a wide grin, "Fly? Man, do you see any wings growing out of these shoulders? Maybe a horn or two is growing out of the head but no wings. And I promised the Lord if I ever went flying again it would be with *my* wings.''

His friend chuckled at the Pastor's remark. These two men had been close friends for a long time. Nothing makes for closer, deeper ties than the sharing of burdens and problems, and they had shared the problems of a growing thriving church for a long time. Together they had laughed over the peculiarities of people when some humorous situation developed. And together they had wept and prayed over tragedies and sorrows and burdens — the personal ones and those that occurred among the members of the church they both loved deeply. Therefore John understood his Pastor, and when he saw the sparkle in his eyes and the grin on his countenance he knew that something worth listening to was behind the cryptic words he had just heard.

"All right. Let's hear it. I know when you get that look on your face a yarn is coming up," he said with mock reproach.

The Pastor grew serious. "There is no yarn about this, John," he said. "The fact is, one of the most interesting and frightening experiences of my life is involved in it. I really meant it when I told you I promised the Lord I would use *my* wings the next time I decided to fly. Of course, I made the reservation that if some situation developed that required it, like this other time I will tell you about in a moment, I would trust Him and take off."

John lifted his hand in protest. He said, "Spare me the nonessentials and get to the story, friend."

"All right, John. This one is a dilly, so maybe we ought to get another cup of coffee."

When John had complied with two steaming refills, the Pastor settled back in his chair, stretched his long legs before him more comfortably and began —

"Well, John, you know Ronald Talbot of our church, don't you?"

John was sipping his coffee so he only nodded his head in response to the question.

"Now, you may not know it, but Ronald was once quite a rounder. He hasn't been a Christian but a few years."

John broke in, "That's surprising! That fellow is one of the most sincerely spiritual men I have ever known. I thought he had been a Christian most of his life."

"Yes, you would think so," the Pastor agreed. "But you see, when he got converted, the Lord really got all of him at one time. Ronny has really meant business about following Christ from that moment."

His dark eyes took on a pensive look for a moment, then

began to twinkle as he added, "He surely ought to mean business after what both of us went through for him to meet the Lord."

"Don't stop now, quit stalling and tell me what happened," Newland said with exasperation.

"Well, John, it began one day when Ronald invited me to go grouse hunting with him. I had dropped into his place of business a time or two to give him an invitation to come to church. Oh, he was cordial enough, even seemed to be glad I stopped by, but he always had some pretty ironclad excuses for not being able to attend church. The main thing he said was that Sunday was the big day of the week in his business and that he just couldn't afford to take any time off when he was making the most money.

"I didn't argue with him, but one day I got a little irritated at hearing him talk like that and I said to him, Mr. Talbot, there are some things more important than making money."

"Quick as a flash he returned, 'Name me just one, Preacher.' "

"You know, John, he has five children so I answered him, 'I can't give you their names, but you have five reasons at home and all five of them are far more important than your prosperity. The fact is I doubt if any one of the five has been in Sunday school or church a dozen times in his life.'

"He got the point all right, John. And for once he didn't argue or make excuses. Now, I didn't know it at the time, but do you know what that rascal was hatching up for me?"

John Newland silently shook his head.

"Why, he was working on a scheme to test out my own faith to see if I really meant business or was just acting professional when I talked to him about the Lord and the church. Well, that day he invited me to go grouse hunting. I jumped at the chance, as innocently as a lamb. Ronald drove up in front of my house in that jeep of his and off we went.

"Now, I knew those little machines would do the impos-

56

sible, but Ronny put his through some impossible impossibilities that day. He drove that thing up a log trail that goes up the side of old Paint Lick mountain and put it in climbs and curves and dips where I would have sworn a centipede could not have gone. It had rained the day before and in places that old trail was just bare mud. Sometimes that jeep headed down an incline and just slid forty or fifty feet. Brother, I tell you more than once the hair on my head stood straight up! I noticed from time to time that Ronald was cutting his eyes in my direction, but he didn't say anything and I didn't, either.

"Finally we reached the part of the mountain he planned to hunt, and we got out. The ground sure felt good under my boots. We hunted for several hours without putting up a single grouse and I was tuckered out and ready to call it a day. But not Ronald. He had other plans, so down the mountain we came, slipping and sliding and skidding. I tell you I was just about ready to offer to lighten the load by getting out and walking when we finally reached a degree of safety near the foot of the mountain."

"Is that when you wished for wings, Pastor?" John asked with a soft laugh.

"Stop interrupting, John. You wanted to hear this story, so let me tell it." The smile on the minister's face belied the severity of his words.

"When we got down off the mountain, Ronald said he knew where another trail ran along the bottom of a narrow valley that was full of grouse. I agreed to give it a try. Sure enough, the trail was there. It was pretty well grown up, but at least it was fairly level. We drove to a place where the trail ended and then got out and walked. There was a little brook a couple of yards wide that ran all down that valley and we hadn't gone far before the foot path we were following crossed the stream. Ronald didn't have on any boots, just high top shoes. He was about to turn back because the water was too deep for him to wade, so I carried him across

57

piggyback. He was quite impressed, especially when I helped him across the stream in about a dozen places when the path crossed it. He mentioned it repeatedly and finally he remarked as we returned to the jeep, 'I guess I will have to come to church Sunday to repay you for the times you gave me a lift.'

" 'Ronald,' I told him, 'you don't owe me anything for the little help I gave you, but you come to church Sunday. You will get another kind of lift.'

"And you know," the Pastor continued, "that next Sunday there he was, with his wife and their five children, all of them with that strange, uneasy look of people who haven't been to church for so long they evidently feel that everybody is looking at them."

The Pastor straightened up in his chair, his eyes flashing as he touched again a matter that was always a sore spot to him. "John," he said with heated tones, "when are those of us who are long-time Christians and regular church-goers going to practice a little Christian courtesy and stop making people who haven't been to church for a long time feel like they are out of place?

"This is beside the point of the story, but I worked for a year to get a fellow to come to our church and the first Sunday he came some blow-hard goes up to him and shouts for all to hear, 'Well, well, look who has come to church this morning! Somebody nail down the roof. There must be a tornado coming to make him decide to attend church.' I felt like using my number nine shoe where it would do the most good. Of course, that poor fellow never came back.

"Excuse me, John, for sermonizing. You know that is a pet peeve of mine," the Pastor said more calmly.

"Speak on, Brother." Newland grinned his appreciation for the fire that was always ready to spring into a flaming defense when his minister saw someone hurt or humiliated. "I am with you all the way on that score."

The Pastor settled back in his chair again. He took up where he had interrupted himself. "Anyway, I am glad no one said such a thing to Talbot and his family that first Sunday. Maybe you will remember, John, he came several times after that. Then one Sunday after services he stopped me on the sidewalk outside the church and said, 'Preacher, I am going to fly down to Tennessee in my plane to get some parts for my business. How about going with me?"

"I thanked him and politely excused myself. I had no desire to *fly* anywhere with him after that jeep trip. I remember that he looked at me with scorn on his face and said sarcastically, 'What's the matter, Preacher? Are you afraid?'

"I didn't want to hurt his feelings or to offend him, but to tell you the truth, John, I just didn't want to go," said the Pastor, his brow furrowed with the earnest intensity of his words. "I had never been up in an airplane, and I didn't want the first time to be in any two-bit plane especially with anyone as reckless as Ronald at the controls, so I was all prepared to wiggle out of it somehow. Then he hit me where it hurt.

" 'You preached this morning on what faith will do,' he said. 'Now why don't you practice what you preach? You're not fooling me. You're just plain scared to go with me. I kind of thought there wasn't much to this religious deal you've been trying to hand me.'

"I knew he was needling me and he surely was succeeding. But I also detected sincerity in the way he spoke. So I said, 'All right, Mr. Talbot, if it will convince you that this "religious deal" as you call it is for real, I'll go with you. But I warn you, when we are together up there in the middle of nowhere, I am going to talk to you about your soul because I am going to prove to you that as far as I am concerned, this thing of trusting Christ is real.'

"That sort of set him back for a moment, John, but he couldn't back out now and after some hesitation he agreed to

59

my terms.

"The next day the weather was rough. It rained a gust that morning and when it cleared up the wind was really blowing. We drove out to a cow pasture where Ronald kept his plane and that is when he really began to get close to me. He did everything he could to scare me out of my wits before I even got into that contraption. He told me that he had been having engine trouble and that he hoped it was fixed now. He said it as though he had serious doubts about it, though. Then he noticed the wind, and again with that half skeptical tone he said, 'I guess we can make it out of here in this wind.'

"By that time I was set to say, 'Brother, if you want to call off this trip, I am willing,' but I gritted my teeth and prayed and kept quiet.

"The next thing almost got me, though. He asked me how much I weighed. When I told him, he did some verbal arithmetic just loud enough to be certain I heard him. He added my weight and his and the weight of the load of gasoline and estimated the wind velocity and computed the distance we would have to travel before the plane was airborne against the length of the cow pasture, looked doubtfully at the stock wire fence at the end of the field and summed it all up — looking at me — and said, 'Well, let's try it anyway. We may be able to make it.'

"Brother, I am glad he didn't know how heavy my heart was at that moment because I don't think he would have tried it if he had added that load to his calculations."

The Pastor chuckled at his own words and John added his own grin.

"Of course, John, all of that was designed to shake me up good and proper, and it worked. I am glad Ronald didn't ask me to repeat portions of my sermon on faith while standing there in that cow pasture. Well, we got off all right, cleared the fence with plenty of room to spare, as I should have known we would. However, I still did not know the extent to

60

which Ronald planned to put my faith to the test. Next he wondered if we could get enough altitude to clear the mountain ahead, and then he hoped that sudden downdraft would not make us crash. At last we we flying serenely along and he commented, 'Now, Preacher, isn't this fun? Why don't you let go of that seat? You can't fall out. Just sit back and relax.'

"Maybe I could have relaxed a little, except for his next remarks. He said, 'Man, I hope this engine doesn't act up again. It had some water in the carburetor the other day. I think I got it all out, but —' Then he sort of grinned and said, 'Oh well, one thing about these little planes, if the motor conks out you can glide a long ways until you can locate a field. Maybe we ought to look around down there and pick us out a field in case we have to make a forced landing.' "

The Pastor looked at his friend with amusement. He said, "John, I made myself look down, swallowed my heart that had suddenly come up into my throat, and what do you think I saw? Why, I saw a field, of course. There was only one and it had a lot of white stones in it, no bigger than dots. I wondered to myself if the plane could land in a field full of stones, and then suddenly it dawned on me, as I saw the orderly pattern those stones made, that the field I was looking at was a cemetery.

"Old Ronald saw me looking at it and he laughed out loud and said, 'Preacher, that would be a pretty good one to land in, wouldn't it? They wouldn't have to take us to the cemetery, we would be there already!'

"He just guffawed with laughter. John, I'll tell you what is a fact. I couldn't even laugh a peep."

By this time Newland was also practically rocking with laughter. "Pastor," he finally managed to say, "I can just picture you looking over the side of that cockpit and seeing that cemetery."

The Pastor grinned and said, "I can laugh about it now, but all I could do was pray at that moment. And you haven't heard the worst of it yet. Listen to what followed. We were cruising along. Ronald wasn't saying much. I guess he figured he had better let up on me a little. Anyway, to take my mind off of that so-called landing field we had seen, I began to ask questions about how an airplane is piloted. Ronald gave out a lot of information about the principles of flying and then he said that the best way he could answer my questions was to show me. He told me to put my hands on a wheel that was in front of me and as he moved the wheel he was holding, I could get the movement of the one in my hands. He showed me some pedals down near the floor and told me to put my feet on those. Then he demonstrated the part they played in flying the little plane.

"Well sir, you could have knocked me over with a feather at his next words. 'Preacher, do you think you can fly this thing?' I said, 'Man, are you out of your mind?' All he said was, 'If it flies, you are going to fly it because I am turning it over to you.'

"And with that he turned loose the wheel and took his feet off those pedals.

"Brother, I'm telling you that was a time. He just looked out of the window and started whistling and left me to *fly* that thing. John, you have seen me sweat while I was preaching on a hot day. You haven't seen anything. You should have seen me *that* day. How long I flew the plane I don't know. Eternity seemed a whole lot more real than time just then. Finally he must have figured he had better take the controls back again. When I finally turned loose that wheel, I had been holding it so hard it took me fifteen minutes to straighten my fingers."

The Pastor held his hand out in front of him and flexed the fingers as though still aware of the cramps that had stiffened them during the exciting experience he had just related.

As he paused, John broke in, "That was a foolhardy thing for Talbot to do. Suppose you had lost control of the plane."

"Well, John," the Pastor replied with a sardonic grin, "in that case I would *have* my own wings now."

Again he took up the narrative of his story.

"Shortly after that, Ronald climaxed all that he had done. 'Now that you know how to fly a plane, Preacher,' he said, 'you might as well learn what a plane like this is capable of doing.' And with that he began to put that little thing through its paces. I couldn't begin to tell you all he did. My stomach would rise up one moment and I could have stepped on it the next. My heart went into steeper dives than the plane and I am sure my heart beat faster than the motor was running. Brother, you talk about praying, I really prayed!

"And seriously, John, a wonderful thing happened. All of a sudden there was Someone else in that cockpit. I wasn't afraid any more. I believe Ronald could have turned the plane wrong side out and I wouldn't have been afraid.

"It is wonderful what Jesus does when He comes to your heart in a crisis time like that. I remember I turned to Talbot and said above the roar of the engine, "Go ahead and wring it out if you want. I am not scared anymore. Maybe you don't know it, but you just took on another Passenger.'

"He got control of the plane, leveled it off and asked, 'What do you mean by another passenger?' I told him how my Master had come in response to my frightened prayer and I saw the tears start into his eyes and heard him whisper, 'Then it *is real.*'

" 'Yes, Ronald, it *is* real,' I assured him. 'I should say *He* is real and I want you to know Him. Here you are flying thousands of feet above the earth, and all that is holding us up here physically speaking is that little motor that's churning and that propeller that's flying and these fragile wings. If those things were to disintegrate, you know what would happen. We would both go plummeting to the earth. I am sure when we crashed *I* would be just as dead as you. But what would come after that, Ronald? Have you seriously thought about that question?'

"He didn't say anything. I guess he couldn't right then. He was deeply moved. I continued to talk to him, John. I told him about the Saviour's love and forgiveness. I explained to him how he could surrender his heart to Christ. I helped him to see that he should have no difficulty trusting the Lord with his soul inasmuch as he already knew how to trust that fragile little plane with his life. He got the point.

"Finally I said to him, 'Ronald, if you will put your all in His hands, like you are trusting in this airplane, without fear, without reservation, something wonderful will happen in your soul. And best of all, you don't have to seek Him. He is already here.'

"I heard him say, 'I know He is, and I want to belong to Him.'

"I said, 'Ronald, just go ahead and tell Him that. I can't tell you what to say, but however you put it, He will understand your heart. Now just forget I am here and you talk to Him about this matter.'

"He started praying, John, and it was too wonderful for me to listen. I felt like an intruder. It just rolled out of him like a torrent of pent-up need and hunger. His heart melted, John. You know how it happens. You have seen it come to others. Oh, it was glorious when he started coming out of the depths of his despair and remorse. There was joy in his words as bright and shining as that sky all around us. He was almost singing toward the end of his prayer. Even the engine in that plane sounded like it had a song.

"John, it is wonderful to introduce someone to Jesus and then watch Him take over and melt their heart into surrender and love and claim them for His own. Three of us flew into Tennessee and three of us flew home again, but one of us was different. Old Ronald said to me as the plane came to rest in that cow pasture, 'I feel like I have wings on my heart.' I guess he did have, John. I know my heart had wings that

man leaning against the brick building. He saw that in spite of the studied air of relaxation and indolence, there was a razor-sharp readiness about him. That lean, hard body could whip erect in a flash and be prepared to meet any eventuality. Beneath the surface of ease the minister recognized in the man a tautness and an edginess that made him think of finely tempered steel that could be bent but would instantly spring back when released.

He knew that the tales told about this man were almost legendary. Known far and wide as Ol' Dan Robelin, he could out-fight, out-cuss, out-shoot, out-hunt, out-fish, and out-talk almost anyone in all the hill country round about. It was said that Ol' Dan started working in a sawmill before he was dry behind the ears and from the beginning he did a man's work, a man's cussing and a man's fighting. He had clawed his way through the years of back-breaking labor until everyone who knew him respected him, and not a few feared him — with good reason, too, as cut lips and broken noses and knocked-out teeth would attest. Any Saturday night with Dan Robelin in town, during the tender years of his youth, was bound to produce a roaring, brawling show for any and all who cared to follow in his path.

Hardened by the years in the woods, Ol' Dan was ready when he was offered a job climbing poles and stringing wire as a member of a power company construction crew cutting a swath across the mountains and the valleys and bringing lights to homes and hamlets that had never known any illumination but candles and kerosene lamps. Dan had not been with the construction crew long before he had cussed and fought his way to the top man in the gang. And before long the men who worked with him were boasting that Ol' Dan could put on a pair of climbing spikes and give a squirrel a ten-foot start and then beat the squirrel to the top of the pole. The men loved to tell of times when Dan's climbing spikes would accidentally break loose from the wood into which they had been plunged, how he would slide down the pole, spikes gouging and ripping great slivers of wood, and how he would catch another hold with uncanny skill and race up the pole again, and all during the mad and dangerous scramble not even momentarily would he cease the stream of conversation and banter he had been carrying on with other members of the construction gang.

Hearing the approaching footsteps of the Pastor now, Dan's keen blue eyes peered from beneath the cap brim with a penetrating stare. There was a deceptively slight stiffening of the slouching form, like a cat pretending indifference even while tightening its sinews for the pounce upon its prey.

As the Pastor paused before Dan, he addressed him with tones of respect. "Mr. Robelin," he said, "I have heard a great deal about you. I have wanted to meet you for quite a while, but it seems our paths have not crossed until now." As he spoke, he extended his hand to Dan Robelin. The hand which met his was hard and calloused and gripped his own in a bone-crushing grasp. The Pastor introduced himself and chatted idly with his new acquaintance for several minutes before stating his purpose. Supposing Dan to be at ease again, he said, "Mr. Robelin, I want to invite you to attend our church."

Just as he suspected, the laziness dropped from Dan Robelin instantaneously. In a flash his tall, lean body had come away from the wall and whipped erect. The lined face became sullen, the thin lips grew tight.

"What did you say, Preacher?" The sharp twangy voice fairly exploded. "What did you say?"

The Pastor was unruffled by the explosive words. He calmly repeated himself, "I said I would like to invite you to attend our church, Mr. Robelin. Many of your friends belong there. I have heard them talk about you a great deal. They seem to have a warm affection for you, and I know they would also be delighted to have you attend their church."

68

There was still an incredulous look on Ol' Dan's face as he said, "Well, I'll be —" The Pastor knew that except for respect for his office as a minister the rest of that exclamation would not have been omitted. Robelin shook his head as though to clear his brain. "Well, I *will* be —" he said again, this time speaking to himself.

The Pastor steeled himself for a storm that he knew instinctively was sure to break. For a moment, however, he was thrown off guard as he saw the man's icy blue eyes begin to crinkle at the corners with the beginning of a smile. The smile grew into a chuckle that started way down deep in the barrel chest. It came out sort of a strangled giggle and increased until it became a roar of laughter. Dan Robelin stood there and rocked with mocking laughter until the tears trickled down the seams in his face, like rivulets of rain water creeping across dry, cracked earth.

Then suddenly as the gales of laughter began, they ceased. Dan sucked in a long breath, gently poked the Pastor in the shoulder with a bony finger and said with a voice that fairly crackled with animosity, "Preacher, you want *me* to come to your church?" His eyes blazed with the fires of suppressed fury for a moment. He almost choked as he said, "Do you want me to tell you what I think of you and your whole hypocritical bunch of so-and-so's? Mister Preacher, I can curl the hair on your chest by telling you what I know about that bunch and what I think of them."

He opened his mouth to give expression to the hair-curling thoughts that burned in his mind, then shut it so suddenly his teeth snapped together. With a visible effort he fought for self-control. When he spoke again, it was to himself more than to the man who stood patiently before him. "No— — no," he said, "you are a preacher. I suppose you meant well. I'll just keep my trap shut."

Quite unexpectedly his face was lighted by a warm smile. "Preacher," his voice was gay now, "my church is out there." His strong brown hand pointed past the street, the buildings, the town, toward the hills and valleys that sprawled in every direction. "Yes, sir, there is my church. Out there the wind in the trees preach sermons, the streams sing hymns, the rocks are the pews and the fish, the birds and the animals are the congregation. I'll tell you what, Preacher, why don't you come with me to my church?"

"All right, Mr. Robèlin," the Pastor replied immediately, "you say when."

Dan was taken back by the prompt acceptance. His eyes half squinted with wariness, as though he were trying to peer beneath the exterior of the calm features before him and discover some hidden motive behind the words, some trick perhaps. For a long moment he studied the Pastor's face before he ventured a reply. At last he said resignedly, "I never thought I would see the day Ol' Dan — with a blankety-blank preacher." He filled in the blanks and in spite of himself the Pastor cringed at the cold, disdainful blasphemy. If Dan noticed it, he made no comment. Turning away abruptly he called over his shoulder, "I'll call you, Preacher."

Actually the Pastor thought, as he watched the tall lithe figure walk away, that his brief encounter with Dan Robelin had come to a sudden and complete ending at that moment. Therefore, he was genuinely surprised when he answered the clamor of the telephone the following Saturday morning and the twangy drawl of Robelin's voice greeted him. "Hi, Preacher, I've been thinking this might be a good day to go to church — my church. How about it?"

Before the Pastor's mind flashed pictures of things he had counted on doing that day. He almost groaned aloud as he thought of having to double his efforts on another day if he took this one off. One thing was certain, however. He had his chance with Robelin now and there might not be another. He shrugged aside the demands of a crowded schedule and answered, "Sure, Mr. Robelin. I can be ready in a few minutes. By the way, what does a fellow wear when he goes with you to church? I want to be properly dressed," he added with a bantering note. A chuckle sounded over the wire. "Preacher, I know where there is a stream that has bass as big as a hand saw. I have heard that you are a fisherman so you can take it from there. I'll pick you up in a few minutes." The click of the receiver ended the conversation.

The Pastor had put on his fishing clothes and his hip boots and was sitting on his front steps with his fly rod and tackle beside him when Dan drove up. "Let's go, Mister Preacher," he called. Even though his words sounded cheerful and natural, there was a mocking note, a scornful sharpness in the slight emphasis given to the "mister."

Dan drove rapidly, long brown hands wheeling the car around the sharp turns of the mountain road with dexterity and careless skill. After a few miles on the highway, he turned the car onto a narrow gravel road that headed toward the looming black bulk of a great mountain. Loose rocks picked up by the tires were a staccato clatter against the fenders as the little car sped along. All the while Dan was also clattering away, carrying on a rapid fire, and for the most part, a one-sided conversation. With relish he told of the trophy-size bass he had taken from the stream where they were to fish that day. Boasting was as natural with him as breathing. He was the best fisherman in those parts, he knew he was, and he wanted everyone else to know it also.

Although most of Dan's talk was about himself and about his ability, strangely enough the Pastor did not find the bragging offensive, but listened intently and with fascination. This man was merely stating facts about himself. From time to time Dan's words were punctuated with profanity. There was no intention of trying to make an impression with his strong language; it was the way the man had always talked, the only way he knew to express himself.

71

Without a pause in the rapid flow of his words, Dan suddenly swerved the car and headed straight up a steep grass-covered hill. There was no road to follow here, not even a wagon track. He just headed the automobile at the steep incline and gave it the gas. The motor whined its protest over the hard pull, the wheels bounced and bumped over the uneven ground. Dan's tall frame leaned forward almost touching the steering wheel as though spurring the car to greater effort. The Pastor just clung to whatever his hands could find to hold onto. Cresting the hill, the driver slammed the car to a skidding halt and while it still rocked from the sudden stop, Robelin pointed ahead and said, "Preacher, there is my church. What do you think of it?"

The Pastor gasped audibly at the spectacular beauty that stretched before them as far as the eye could see. At the foot of the hill a mile-wide valley began, running parallel to the great overshadowing mountain that rose loftily, majestically on the far side. Mile after mile the valley sprawled before them. Here and there groves of trees blended their darker hues with the startling greenness of the deep, lush growth of the grass. Small bands of black cattle dotted the valley. Like a silver ribbon a rambling stream cut a shimmering swath across the verdant carpet. With amazed appreciation the Pastor's eyes followed the course of the river and the graceful flowing lines of the mountain until they were both lost in the blue haze of the distance. Finally, with simple reverence he said, "It's beautiful."

"Yeah," Dan agreed dryly, "I thought you would say so." But he had no time to waste in appreciation of the marvelous beauty of the place. He had come here to fish. Even as he spoke he was scrambling out of the automobile and grabbing at the same time for his tackle. His only comment before he went lunging with long, eager strides down the hill to the river was, "Preacher, if you are waiting for me, you are just wasting your time."

72

The Pastor hastily gathered his fishing gear and took out after his companion. As he walked he tried to pull up the hip boots he wore to their full length. It was quite a task, trying to walk swiftly downhill, juggle the tackle in one hand and pull the boots up all at the same time; no sooner would he succeed in getting one boot in the proper position than the other one would slip down. Grabbing at the rubber, he dropped the flyrod. Scrambling for the rod, he dropped the tackle box, which promptly added to the frustration by popping open and spilling flies and plugs for a dozen feet down the hill. Thoroughly disgusted with himself he managed to restrain his remarks to a fervent ''Phooey!''

By the time the Pastor had collected his wits, his tackle and his patience, Dan was already wading into the swift, clear stream, whipping the slender flyrod with the same careless dexterity with which he did most things. For a moment the Pastor stood watching the line from Dan's rod arching gracefully and falling light as thistledown upon the whirling surface of the river. It was not in him to linger long, however, when there were fish to be caught. By the time he reached the river bank a fever of eagerness had laid hold upon him. He was about to enter the stream, boots fully extended now, when Dan called out, ''Be careful of these rocks, Mr. Preacher. Some of them are slick as soap.''

With a careless wave of his hand, the Pastor returned, ''Don't worry about me, Dan, my feet are big enough to give me a pretty good understanding.'' Nevertheless, he waded gingerly into the cold water, careful to slide his boots across the rocks to test the slipperiness before trusting his considerable weight upon them. Even through the rubber that encased his feet and legs he could feel the stinging cold of the water that swirled about him gurgling its threats at the intrusion. Dan had moved across the river toward the opposite bank and thus abreast the two men moved and fished down the stream.

From time to time, the Pastor let the line float unattended

upon the water while he feasted his eyes and his soul upon the handiwork of the Creator. *Surely,* he thought, *the Lord took delight in making this place. I think He must have lingered awhile here and arranged it just to suit Himself.* Here a red-winged blackbird clung to the swaying stalk of a reed and sang his clear, sweet song of praise. There a shy willow leaned over the sparkling water, seeming to study its graceful reflection in the mirror-like surface. Prompted by a transient breeze it trailed supple, leafy hands into the stream as though to say, 'Thank you for letting me see myself in you.'

Yonder a half-grown frog winked its protruding eyes at a butterfly that was sipping clover nectar a few feet away and tried to sing in a voice that fluctuated half way between falsetto and bass tones. Near the bank a school of flashing minnows played hide-and-go-seek in a thick bed of water cress, venturing out of the protective green forest of vegetation in a silvery swarm and darting back with frantic speed at some suspected shadow. A white heron stood like a frozen statue, a model of marvelous patience, nothing moving about its snowy, graceful figure but its icy eyes. Suddenly its long slender neck whipped forward like a striking snake, plunging its spearlike beak deep in the crystal water. The Pastor chuckled aloud as he saw the heron miss its strike, shake its narrow head to remove the clinging crystal drops of water and with dignified disgust stalk off down the stream on its long pipestem legs.

Above the valley an eagle floated lazily along the path of the winds, screamed once, and cupping its wings plummeted off toward its lonesome lair. Over all the flow and drama of life the great mountain kept eternal vigilance like a somber-faced sentinel.

Feeling like an intruder in the quiet serenity and beauty of such a place, the Pastor lifted his face to the cloudless blue heavens and whispered, "Thank You, Lord, for all of this."

Just then Dan let out a squall. "I've got him! I've got him,

74

Preacher. He's as big as a handsaw.'' Beyond a question Robelin had tied into a big one. The supple rod whipped and thrashed the air like a living thing. The taut line snarled through the water with a vengeance as the bass heaved its bulk among the rocks with almost frightening fury. Dan was frantically trying to hold the fish, his craggy face a study of intensity and eagerness. The action was so fast and furious it was almost impossible to follow it. One moment the bass was pulling its way downstream, stripping line from the reel, the next moment it had turned across the current, the combined weight of the battler and the pull of the river against the curving line torturing the little rod almost to the breaking point. With a mad rush the bass spurted up the river again, Dan desperately trying to remove the sudden slack from the line.

The Pastor's shouted words of encouragement were unheard or unnoticed by the intent angler who countered every move of the great fish smoothly and swiftly. No wonder they said Ol' Dan was the best fisherman around. All of his experience and skill were evident now.

But the bass was experienced and skilled, too. This was not the first time he had felt the sting of a hook in his powerful jaw and he was far from being outwitted or overcome. With a mighty lunge he hurled his powerful form toward a granite boulder in midstream. The leader screeched against the rough surface of the rock momentarily. There was a sharp 'spang' as it parted and the line floated lazily and loosely to the top of the water. The wily fish rolled over once, slapped the surface of the water with a tail as wide as a man's hand, showering diamonds of water in every direction, and disappeared.

A look of stunned amazement gripped Ol' Dan's rugged features. He just could not believe that the fish was gone. He paled, his face almost white. Then the fury leaped through him. His face flushed, his eyes flamed, the thin lips twisted into a snarl. Now words began to flow from him in a heated torrent.

The Pastor was glad he was too far away to distinguish the words. He called out solicitously, "Tough luck, Dan. Can I help you get rigged again?"

Dan only glanced briefly in the direction of his companion as he said, "Mr. Preacher, the only thing you can do to help me is to stay out of earshot for the next fifteen minutes."

Now the Pastor was a deeply compassionate individual and he would have been glad to say some sympathizing word or perform some deed of helpfulness that would have dispelled the gloom that had settled on his partner. Because of this he started across the stream, planning to be of any assistance possible. He had taken only a few steps when Dan called out, "Preacher, you can't come over here." His tone of voice was so gruff the Pastor was all the more certain that his disappointed fishing mate needed the comfort and kindness of the ministry, and he kept walking. Dan showed genuine concern as he called out again, "You'd better stay on your side. I tell you that you can't come over here." Prudence might well have listened to the warning; the preacher did not. He kept going — just a step or two farther.

Suddenly the rocks beneath his booted feet were not there any more. Instead he seemed to be treading on a sheet of ice or a coating of grease. Frantically he tried to backtrack, but while his feet scrambled like those of a tap dancer, he was sliding like an avalanche. For several seconds he managed to stay upright while his boots beat a slithering tattoo on the slick shelf of rock and then, *whap,* he struck the water. As he went under and that cold mountain water stung his body, he let out a mighty "whoosh." Carried by the swift current he came up about ten feet below the point of catastrophe, splashing and sputtering like a porpoise, teeth chattering like the hail on a tin roof. What a bedraggled sight he made as he pulled himself painfully from the water onto the solid footing of another rock! The worst wound from the experience was ruptured pride and injured dignity.

As he stood there shivering and dripping Ol' Dan added insult to injury by jeering, "I told you you couldn't wade down across there."

The Pastor drew himself, with what dignity he could muster, onto the grassy bank of the river, laid down the rod to which he still clung, pulled off his boots and emptied them of gallons of water and proceeded to try to bring some semblance of respectability to his disheveled appearance. And he did not exactly appreciate the fact that Dan was grinning so widely his dark face seemed likely to split.

With evident determination to suppress the mirth that threatened momentarily to erupt and get out of hand, Robelin approached the Pastor saying, "If you think you have got sufficient understanding in those wet feet, Mister Preacher, to get back across that river, I guess we had best go to the car and take you home for some dry clothes." He paid no attention to the half-hearted protests from the minister, so together they maneuvered the stream, carefully avoiding the slick shelf of rocks, and soon were headed for home.

The Pastor did not say much during the return trip, although Dan kept up his usual rapid fire monologue. For charity's sake he made no mention of the preacher's disaster until they were parting. Then, an impish grin on his expressive face, he called after the Pastor, "Preacher, I knew you would like my church, but I hardly thought you would like it so well you would get baptized in order to join it!" With a merry laugh and a wave of his hand he was off.

The Pastor, still ashamed of the spectacle he had made of himself in the presence of the man he had desired so much to impress, muttered to himself as he climbed the steps to his home, "Ol' Dan Robelin, you're going to have to eat those words."

Of course the whole town knew the story of the Pastor's

"baptism" by the next day and the citizens found a rare delight in it. Realizing that there was no point in trying to avoid the joshing that was sure to come, the Pastor boldly took his usual daily stroll down the main street. He had not progressed far until Bill James hurried out of his store greeting the minister with, "Pastor, I understand you're going to become the preacher in another church." Then with a sly grin he added, "Ol' Dan told me about you being baptized in *his* church." With a booming laugh he slapped his beloved Pastor on the back and turned away to his business.

Joe Jenkins took the next crack at the preacher. He had seen the Pastor approaching and from somewhere he obtained a towel which he proffered as he came near, mock concern hiding the laughter that was bubbling in him. "Here, brother," he said in doleful tones of pretended sympathy, "dry yourself off and come inside. I know that water must have nearly frozen you." The laughter would stay down no longer. With his arms about the Pastor's shoulders his joyous whoops of mirth echoed up and down the busy street.

Patiently the Pastor endured the friendly ribbing and moved on. Old Milt Downey came to the door of his service station as the Pastor passed and cackled, "Hey there, Pastor. We have a special on tire chains today or maybe we can retread those hip boots and provide more traction." Still cackling gleefully, he waved a friendly hand before returning to his affairs.

So it went, and for many days the Pastor's face was red. But there was no resentment in him. Rather, he realized that the ties of friendship had been strengthened by his ordeal and the enjoyment his friends got from it. In his heart he was glad they loved him enough to laugh with him and at him and more than once he said in his heart, "I thank You, Lord, that they don't put me on a pedestal and that I can be one with my people."

For several days the Pastor did not even catch a glimpse of

Ol' Dan but when they finally met again they each knew instinctively that they had become fast friends and the warm strong handclasp with which they greeted each other was symbolic of the deep, strong ties that would bind them together for life. From then on they made it a point to spend at least a few minutes together almost daily. In these two men friendship reached its highest level; the point where it was not expressed in getting but in giving. Whatever the one possessed, the other could have merely for the asking.

Yet, sometimes the Pastor's heart ached because his love for Christ, the thing he desired most to share with Ol' Dan, was coldly refused and rebuffed whenever it was even mentioned. Naturally, he made the effort. He and Dan had known each other intimately for only a short while when the minister made the first appeal for Christ. The time he chose surely seemed ideal.

It was one of those hours so filled with the evidence of God that it seemed impossible for anyone to miss the majesty and glory of His presence. Together they sat on Dan's front porch. For once Ol' Dan had nothing to say. He sat in his favorite chair, feet propped up on the porch rail before him, his eyes half closed and dreamy looking, his sharp, hard features softened in relaxation. Whatever the thoughts that held him in silence, he kept them to himself.

To the Pastor the quietness was appropriate. Once again he was spellbound by the mighty display of the glory of God in the work of His fingers. Twilight had come on soft, swift feet. Beyond the rolling hills, Old Knobby, the great dark mountain, had pulled a mantle of purple haze about its massive shoulders. Beyond its rim a red-eyed sun took a final look over the hills before it hurried down the horizon, lest it be delinquent in its mission of awakening other distant lands. In the fading light, distance lost something of its dimensions and the lesser hills seemed to draw closer to the foot of the mountain, huddling there for shelter and comfort during the dark. The grim old mountain held the evening star aloft to reassure the crowding hills that it would not be too dark through the night. Then it loosed the cloak of purple twilight from its shoulders and let it spill down its slopes to cover the hills and valleys below.

It was then the Pastor chose to give expression to the words that were throbbing in his mind. In a voice made soft and low by the splendor of God, he quoted, "I will lift up mine eyes unto the hills, from whence cometh my help. My help cometh from the Lord, which made heaven and earth."[1] The words came naturally, with no intent to be impressive or dramatic. They were in his heart; he had to speak them.

Dan Robelin, deep in his own thoughts and only half hearing, stirred in his chair and murmured, "What did you say?"

"I was just thinking out loud, I guess," the Pastor replied. "Maybe I was quoting the sermon I just heard that old mountain preach."

Dan was fully alert now. His feet slid from the railing with a resounding thud. He was suddenly, stiffly erect in his chair, body poised as though for flight. Sharp suspicion made him tense as he demanded, "What are you talking about, Preacher?" he growled.

The abrupt change in Ol' Dan was lost to the Pastor who still had his eyes and his heart fixed on distant scenes. Without turning his head he said, "Dan, I just don't see how a man can watch what we have just seen and not know that there is a loving God who made all of this."

The statement was so matter-of-fact, so real to him that he was totally unprepared for his friend's reaction. Dan leaped to his feet, eyes narrow and blazing, grim face twisted with resentment, his lanky figure in a half crouch as though ready to grapple with an opponent. At his side gnarled fists were knotted, ready to strike. "Preacher" — the word whipped out — "that's *enough*. We are friends and I want it to stay that way. But believe me, it won't stay that way unless you keep your religion to yourself.''

The Pastor's face blanched before the fury he saw in Robelin. What had he said? What had he done? Alarm filled him, and despair clutched at him as these questions raced through his mind. Surely it could not be! This man was his friend. Why could they not share the love of another Friend? As the realization dawned upon him that they were poles apart even though friends, tears stung his eyes and his heart ached and yearned for Ol' Dan to know his Christ.

If Robelin noticed the hurt and longing in the minister's eyes, he gave no indication of it. Consumed by his anger, he turned his back on the preacher and his fist crashed down upon the railing of the porch. From that position he said with venomous quietness, ''If I ever want to know anything about your God or your religion, I will let you know. Until I do, just keep it to yourself.''

Without a word the Pastor stood up, gazed sorrowfully at the stubborn back of his friend for a moment, and walked away. Much of that night was spent in prayer and in the searching of his own soul. Never could he fail, as he felt he had failed tonight, without a deep sense of self-reproach. With all his heart he desired to belong so completely to the Saviour that he could say with another who was completely surrendered, ''. . . I live; yet not I, but Christ liveth in me. . . .''[2]

During the slow, tortured hours of the night, he alternately paced the room or knelt before God. There came the time when he cried unto the Lord, ''Have I hidden Christ from the eyes of my friend? Has pride or self-righteousness or any such thing obscured my Saviour so that one so close to my heart as Dan cannot take knowledge that I have been with Jesus? Have I not prayed enough? Have lesser things meant more to me than the soul of this man? O God, O God! Show me how I failed. Give me another chance.'' For a long time his very soul was scourged by remorse and self-reproach.

And then came Jesus, and a hand touched the Pastor's grieving heart, the hand that will not break even the bruised reed. With a love, an understanding, a gentleness that a thousand tongues could never describe, the hand of Christ dried up the tears and lifted the ache from the broken and contrite heart. And the man's weary and tragic face lifted and lighted and the smile that wreathed it was the reflection of His glory. The Pastor knew deep within that he would have another chance and someday his friend Jesus and Ol' Dan would be friends, too.

Yet as the days stretched out into years there was never a sign that Dan Robelin would give in. Always he parried every effort as skillfully as a fencer. He slammed shut every door of conversation which the Pastor opened, in regard to the church or anything spiritual. Sometimes he stormed out rudely. Again he might head off the advances with a grim look of warning or a grin that twisted with sarcasm. Whatever method he used to silence his friend, Ol' Dan was always successful. Many times the Pastor was deeply hurt. But he prayed without ceasing that the time would come when he could introduce Dan to Jesus. Never for a moment did he doubt that the prayer would be answered. Someday, somehow the tough armor of cynicism and rebellion would be penetrated. Somewhere there was a shaft of love or concern or friendship that would find a vulnerable spot.

As time swept on, Ol' Dan still out-cussed, out-fished, out-talked anyone in the hill country round about. However, where the Pastor was concerned, his respect was usually evident. He guarded his words and seldom gave vent to the explosive oaths that were so characteristic of him at other times. Perhaps this self-control was not of his own choosing, but he had soon learned that if he was to continue to enjoy the companionship of the man he had come to love, he had to lay his profanity aside, at least while in the minister's presence.

There was one time when Dan ripped out a blistering oath that struck chills up the Pastor's spine as he heard it. When such a thing had occurred previously, the Pastor had bitten his lips and remained silent, biding his time. He would say to himself, *Dan Robelin, my Saviour is going to change your way of talking when you get to know Him before long.* But as it became more evident that Ol' Dan's heart was as hardened as ever, he realized that one of two things must take place; either the cussing had to end or the companionship would. He could no longer stand silently by while the name of his Friend was taken in vain. Thus it was when the vehement oath ripped out of Dan's thin-lipped mouth, the Pastor's eyes flamed. He placed himself directly in front of the blasphemer and fixing his eyes sternly upon him he said, "Dan Robelin, you have forbidden me to speak the name of my God in praise while I am in your presence. Now I demand that you stop using His name in profanity while you are in mine."

Caught in complete surprise by the sudden outburst from the usually quiet and mild-mannered minister, Dan looked sheepish at first, a sickly grin sliding tentatively across his sharp features. Then as it dawned upon him that someone, anyone, had *demanded* something from him, his lean form stiffened, his face settled into hard lines, and the fury began to whip through him. Unflinchingly the Pastor's eyes gripped and held him. For a moment it seemed that the ties of friendship would snap with the strain. Then Dan relaxed, grinned sardonically and said, "Mister Preacher, I reckon you are the first man who ever demanded anything of Ol' Dan and got away with it." A merry chuckle rumbled from his barrel chest. He slapped the minister on the shoulder and added, "You know, I like you for it. Stick to your guns, Preacher. If ever I cuss again around you it will be accidental, and not intentional."

There were other signs of a softening of Dan's cast-iron makeup. The Pastor seized on each one with renewed hope and exploited it to the fullest in an effort to reach the heart of the man for Christ. Always, always he failed. Dan Robelin would go with him to catch fish, but he was one fisherman who was determined never to be caught.

As a year passed, then two, the Pastor realized that his only chance was to be a living sermon. If he couldn't talk to Ol' Dan about Christ, he could teach him by his example. Someday that tough old heart was bound to surrender.

And it did! More than four years had passed since these men first met. To all appearances Dan was no closer to becoming a Christian after all that time and association with the preacher than he had been at the beginning. And then one night it happened so unexpectedly, so simply and beautifully, that the Pastor was left aghast.

Ol' Dan had come that day to the parsonage. "I thought you would like to know that my mother is seriously ill," he confided. "I am going to see her this evening and I wondered if you would like to go along. It has been a long time since I saw her, too long I reckon, but I would like for you to meet her if you can go with me." The Pastor agreed to accompany him. He had desired for a long time to learn the kind of home from which this stubborn, defiant man had come.

The journey of some fifty miles through the rugged mountain country was a delightful drive. The torturously twisting road wound through the fertile valleys, sometimes following flashing, brawling streams, sometimes climbing back and forth in sweeping curves up the timbered mountain slopes to the crest of a gap or saddle in the long graceful line of the mountain ranges that loomed up row upon row.

It was twilight when they arrived in the tiny hamlet where Ol' Dan had been born and had lived until he left to beat his determined way in life. The home to which they came at the end of the quiet street was old and mellowed by the years. Dan's swift strides led the way up the rickety steps. The Pastor waited close behind while he rapped once on the door

84

and then opened it, calling out, "Mom, it's Dan!"

From somewhere in the dim recesses of the old house a glad cry responded. "Dan, is it really you? Come in, son."

The Pastor followed his friend into the house and they made their way through the shadowy rooms until they came to the bedroom where the weak but joyful voice was still calling out to them.

On the bed, painfully propped up on one elbow, was a tiny old lady. Her wrinkled face was sheathed with smiles of delight. Tears of pure joy coursed down her cheeks. She struggled to hold herself half propped up on one arm while the other, as thin and trembling as a reed, reached out toward her son. For the first time since he had known him, the Pastor saw tenderness in Dan Robelin. He slipped to his knees beside the bed. Taking the fragile little hand of his mother into his own great ones, he lifted it slowly to his lips and kissed it. Leaning over he gently kissed the old wrinkled cheek. The Pastor, a lump in his throat and tears in his eyes, said to himself, *I knew there was a soft spot somewhere in you, Dan Robelin. I knew it.*

Ol' Dan was strangely quiet during the homeward drive. Ordinarily he rattled on without a break, but that night there were long periods when the only talking was done by the Pastor or else there was no sound but the smooth humming of the car's motor. The preacher concluded that the pensiveness of his companion was caused by anxiety over his mother's illness. If he could have known the thoughts and longings that were seething in Dan's brain and tearing at his very soul, he would have been overjoyed, but there was no outward indication of the inner turmoil that all but locked Robelin's lips with silence. Therefore the Pastor was totally unprepared when suddenly the car swerved to the side of the road and came to an abrupt halt. Dan slumped over the steering wheel soundlessly. Alarmed, the minister asked anxiously, "Are you sick, Dan?" There was no response. It was as if the man had passed out cold. The Pastor took hold of Dan's shoulder and shook him gently. "Quick, Dan, tell me, are you ill?"

This time there was a slight stirring under his hand and a ghastly groan. "Yes" — the word was but a whisper. Deeply disturbed the Pastor searched the darkness. The black night hid everything but the short expanse of the road revealed by the headlights that still burned. *Where will I find a doctor in this lonely and forsaken country?* he thought. He knew they were miles from any town. The best and only solution seemed to be to take the wheel himself and drive to the nearest town, however far that might be, as fast as possible.

Soothingly he said, "My friend, let me help you slide over to this side of the car. I will drive you to a doctor as quickly as I can. Do you have any idea where we could find one anywhere near?"

Robelin partially straightened from his slouching position. He turned his face away from his companion, looking out into the darkness and slowly shook his head.

Believing that every minute might count the Pastor insisted that Dan let him take the wheel.

Still peering out into the black night, his face averted, and with a sound that was a groan and a sob more than words Ol' Dan said, "I'm not that kind of sick. It's in here." His gnarled hand tapped his chest.

Still thinking in terms of physical illness, the Pastor was more alarmed than ever. He thought that the groaning words and the gesture that accompanied them spelled out a heart attack. He was about to demand an exchange of places when the form beside him came fully upright. A long sigh escaped as Robelin turned to face his companion. In the feeble illumination from the dashboard light, the minister saw the silver streak of tears on the leathery features that now faced him.

"What is it, Dan?" he inquired. "I can get you to a doctor if you will let me drive."

Ol' Dan's seamed face twisted with an agonized grimace. The words were as though pried out of him as he said,"Preacher, I don't need a doctor. I need — I need —" Helplessly he shrugged his shoulders. "I don't know what I need. I just know there is *something* I've got to have."

Mystified the Pastor frowned. "Well, Dan," he replied, "I don't know what happened. I don't know what you are talking about, but if you will tell me, I will do what I can, whatever it is." Later he was to rebuke himself for his blindness, but it still had not dawned upon him that the doctor his friend needed and groped for was the Great Physician.

He could scarcely believe what his ears heard next. "Preacher, my heart is in torment. My soul, if I have a soul, is in hell at this moment. I've never felt like this before in my whole life. I just know, all of a sudden, that you have got something that I haven't got and I need whatever it is like I have never needed anything before."

Slowly, incredulously, the light was breaking for the Pastor. He caught his breath with a quick intake and sat in silent awe before the fact that Ol' Dan Robelin was looking for Jesus.

His voice choked as he answered, "Now I see. Oh, Dan, how long have I waited and prayed for this moment! I know what you need and where you can find it."

Dan interrupted him, "I suppose you have tried to tell me many times and I wouldn't let you. How could you be so patient? I know that you have wanted to talk to me about this from the very beginning, and I don't know why I refused to listen. If there is any excuse, it is probably that I was suspicious. A lot of people have talked to me about joining a church, but I knew there were people in any church in our town that I couldn't get along with. They would talk to me about coming to church and then take pride in the fact that I have been the roughest, toughest guy in town. I thought they wanted me to come to church just to brag, 'We got Ol' Dan into our church.' I guess I was wrong about that, but it seemed that way to me.''

Impulsively his hand reached out and covered the pastor's hand that was on the seat beside him. ''But you, my friend, have cared about *me*. Somehow I knew that, but I didn't want to admit it. Preacher, you are the only person, except for my mother, who ever cared enough about me to even try to talk to me about my soul or about Christ. Nobody else ever mentioned Him, just you and my mother.

''I saw her lying there tonight, so sick, so patient and good, still loving me so much in spite of how I have lived and how I neglected her. Then I saw you kneel beside that bed before we left and you took her hand and held it while you prayed for her, and I saw the look of understanding that passed between the two of you when you had finished praying, and it all hit me like a fist pounding into my stomach. I wanted to shout, 'What is it you two have found that I have missed? Who is this Christ you both know and talk about?' I held it back and didn't say anything, but all the way we have come since then I have been looking at myself, the way I have lived — or the way I have not lived — I don't know which haunts me the most right now.''

He broke off at this point and sat quietly with head bowed for long minutes. The Pastor was also silent, knowing that the time for him to speak had not yet come. First, Robelin needed to empty his heart of the bitter dregs that were there.

At last Dan spoke again. ''I have watched you like a hawk, my friend. I watched every move you made and listened to every word you said. I watched you because I didn't believe that religion was anything but hypocrisy and I told myself that you would betray all you stood for sooner or later. You would prove to be a fake. But you fooled me, and finally I began to see that it is all real with you and then I started looking at others and I saw that it was real with them, too. I just hadn't recognized it or wanted to believe it. But now I do, and with all my heart I want whatever it is that you have in your heart and in your life." Humbly he whispered, too overcome to speak any other way, "Please, please tell me how I can have it, too."

The Pastor's heart nearly burst with joy. Wordlessly he cried out within him, *Lord Jesus didst Thou hear? Ol' Dan is calling to Thee. O Lord, come to his heart now. It will soon be thrown wide open.* To Dan Robelin he said quietly and carefully, "It is not something but Some*one* you seek. You just need Jesus, Dan. And He is near. Just ask Him to come into your heart and take over your life. He will do all the rest of it."

Dan's head was flung back. His eyes were closed. His sinewy hands gripped the steering wheel before him. Slowly, painfully, he began to pray. He told Jesus of his life, his sins, his sorrows. The words came faster and faster as though his very soul had been unblocked and every suppressed and hidden longing in him was turning loose. He prayed himself empty. His spiritual hunger, long neglected, was a pleading — "Oh Lord, please forgive me. Help me. Save me. Come to me."

Then came Jesus. It was a glorious moment when he came to the crowds waiting upon another mountain, in the days of His flesh. It was a glorious moment when He came to a humbled Saul of Tarsus on the road to Damascus. It was a glorious moment when He came into the upper room. But the Pastor felt that none of those times could have surpassed the moment when He came to that lonely spot on a mountain road and claimed Dan Robelin's yielded heart and took that life so battered and beaten by sin and began to fashion it anew. Not in a whole lifetime could he ever have described the awe and splendor of that moment. Never in a lifetime or in the endless stretches of eternity could he forget how Jesus came that night.

How long the three of them remained beside that road

neither of the men would ever know. Finally they looked at each other and the smile that passed between them was shining with tears. Spontaneously they reached out their hands. The strong clasp that followed was more than the grip of friend to friend — now it was brother to brother.

The quietness in which they drove home after that was not an empty silence, but a silence that came from a fullness too great for words. Each man thought his own long thoughts of praise and gladness. The thought that filled the Pastor's mind, the joy that flooded his heart, was that a fisherman had been caught. His soul was singing — *Thank You, Lord Jesus. Oh – thank You!"*

Not many days later, the Pastor's cup of joy was running over when he took the hand of Ol' Dan Robelin and baptized him. When the beautiful ceremony was ended the two of them stood for a moment with their arms about each other's shoulders. And Christian people who had prayed long and faithfully for this moment, without Ol' Dan ever knowing it, rejoiced with them. And many a tear-wet face was lifted with a whispered "Thank You, Lord Jesus. Thank You."

[1]Psalm 121:1, 2

[2]Galatians 2:20

6

A MINISTER'S
DESPAIR

THE SLATE-COLORED clouds covered the sky like a sullen
scowl. From the northeast a fitful wind blew damp and cold.
The sun had made a few half-hearted attempts to break
through the overcast and then had seemingly wrapped itself
in a blanket of clouds to keep out the chill wind. As though
angry to be shut off from its view of the sky, the sea spitefully
struck out at the beach.

The gray day matched the Pastor's mood of despair. Not
often did his burdens and cares get the best of him, but this
was one of those rare times when his heart was so heavy he
could not rid himself of the despondency that apparently
moved in to stay. Vainly had he attempted to pray. Equally as
fruitless had been his efforts to find solace in the Word he
loved. The repeated failures had only added to the confusion
within him. Not only did he now have unsolved problems,
but also there was fear in his heart; fear that somehow he had
lost step with the footfalls of his Friend.

That morning when he awakened and beheld the leaden skies and felt a desolation in his heart, he knew that something must be done. Somehow he had to search his soul until it was purged of whatever was blocking the Presence that customarily was a constant, abiding reality. Somehow he must find his Friend again, and in finding Him receive the answers to questions that burned in his mind and burdened his soul.

But how could he find Him? Where should he seek Him? He groaned within as these questions confronted him. Unconsciously he repeated the words that Job spoke out of a heart of agony — "Oh that I knew where I might find him! . . . Behold, I go forward, but he is not there; and backward, but I cannot perceive him: On the left hand, where he doth work, but I cannot behold him; he hideth himself on the right hand, that I cannot see him."[1]

Thus it was that the Pastor happened to be walking along a lonely stretch of beach on this gloomy, raw day. He was oblivious to the scurrying clouds above. Even the loud crashing of the waves did not penetrate his mind, so deep were his thoughts.

"Where and when did it all begin?" he wondered. "Did I misunderstand His will? But it seemed so clear when He spoke. I thought I *knew*. There was no doubt, no uncertainty about it. He *told* me He wanted me to come to this place. I *know* He did. He knew I did not want to leave the hills. I begged Him to let me stay and yet daily it became more definite that He wanted me here."

Suddenly a thought crossed his seeking mind that left him aghast. "Did He misguide me?"

He put the thought from him as if it were an unclean thing. "No, no, that cannot be. O Lord, forgive me. I cannot find You now, but it is my doing, not Yours."

Wearily he sank down onto the sand. A gull hurtled overhead, rocketing on the wind. Something in the creaming foam of the raging sea caught its keen eye. It wheeled into the wind and hung motionless for a long moment as it searched below. Then it turned with the wind again and plummeted off toward the horizon.

The man did not raise his head to look. He sat with his arms folded like a bridge across his knees and his head upon his arms. At his feet the waves crashed and roared. He shuddered, but it was not from the raw dampness of the wind. It was the cold hand of a nameless dread clutching at his heart that made him shiver. His mind picked at long, tangled threads of thought, examining each one briefly to see if perhaps it might lead to the unraveling of the dark dread in him. . . .

He remembered the years of joyous service among the people of the hills, years that were fruitful with accomplishment. From the happy memories he turned his mind to the day when a letter had come from another congregation asking him to be their pastor. At first such a thing seemed unthinkable, and yet he admitted to himself even as he read the letter something within prompted him to take a long slow look at it. The second time he read the words, ''And so our church has voted to ask you to accept a call to become our pastor.'' Abruptly he had folded the pages and almost as if they burned his fingers he dropped them into a drawer on his desk. Even there they spoke to him, however, called out to him with an insistence that could not be denied. Instinctively he knew that another will had decided the vote of that church. Yet, he could not bring himself to admit that this was true. Deliberately he shut his mind against the reality that was becoming more certain by the moment and then he got up and went out.

But how can anyone deny the undeniable or stop the irresistible? The demanding clarity of his Master's insistence came again and again. Sometimes he prayed, other times he refused to let himself pray, for with each time something within took away his peace. Always he knew where this experience would ultimately reach its conclusion. At last, one day he saw that he must surrender. He was not denying his Friend's will, only denying himself the joy and peace without which he could not exist. That was the day he went to his knees with an aching heart. As he tried to say, "Lord, I'll go," a groan of pure agony wrenched loose from his soul. He buried his face in his hands and wept.

Slowly, painfully the words came: "Lord, Thou didst bring me to this place and I was content to come. Thou didst bless me here beyond my hopes. Thou hast walked these hills with me. It has been good, Lord. Thou knowest I do not want to leave my work or my friends here. Yet, I want Thy will to be done. I love Thee, my Master, more than all else."

There was a long pause, then with tears streaming — "Thy will be done." These last words came with a gasp of broken sobbing. But the most difficult thing in his life had been accomplished. No sooner had the words of surrender been uttered than a feeling of indescribable peace flooded the Pastor's soul. The room where he knelt was filled with radiance that was felt rather than seen. His heart hammered and his body shook as a joy that was almost an agony swept his very being.

Thus Moses must have shivered at the burning bush. Thus Isaiah must have felt the day he saw the Lord high and lifted up. Thus the mighty Paul must have been stirred as he fell to the ground on the Damascus road, overwhelmed by the Living Presence. Surely it was something like this that fell upon the disciples on the day of Pentecost.

Never, never had such a tremendous experience come to the Pastor. He felt strong as a giant, yet as helpless to move as an infant. It seemed to him that he must be ten feet tall, but at the same moment so humbled that if he should move he would have to crawl. Oh, it was glorious! How long he remained in the glory of that Presence he never knew.

At last with eagerness the Pastor set his face toward a new and challenging field of service. Beyond any question he knew that he moved in the circle of his Master's will now. There were busy days of packing and preparing to move. Then came the tearful good-byes with people whom he loved and who loved him in their turn. Now he realized how deep the roots of his life had gone among these people of the hills and it began to dawn upon him how much his ministry had meant to them. Every day many people stopped in at the Pastor's home and revealed to him some experience in which he had played an unforgettable part. Warm handclasps, tear-wet faces, words of deep appreciation for some part of himself that had been given unstintingly told eloquently of ties that the years had made firm and fast. Now they must be broken.

The Pastor knew that he was leaving a lot of himself among these people. Each farewell seemed to cut off a little piece of his heart. Yet he knew that there would be other voices giving a welcome among new friends. For every sad handclasp of parting now there would be a glad handshake of welcome soon. So the eagerness of anticipation hurried the Pastor's preparations.

Finally the change was made. For a while there were more frantic days of unpacking and putting belongings in new and strange places. Now the stream of people who visited the Pastor's home came with greetings and good wishes.

Caught up in the crowded days of work and meeting his new congregation, the Pastor had scant opportunity to notice any coolness or reserve on the part of some people he met. Then one day he was brought abruptly and rudely to face the hostility that had gone unnoticed before. Without warning it came. One of the officials of the church dropped in to "meet the new preacher." *Was that a look of disdain upon the man's face?* the Pastor wondered. He soon knew, for this is what he heard.

"Preacher, you might as well know that many people here do not want you. In fact, you are wasting your time unpacking your things. You won't be here long enough to justify the effort. Maybe you don't know it, but the church has run off its last two preachers, and you are going to be run off, too."

The Pastor was stunned by the words. Surely the man was joking. The minister smiled tentatively at the bearer of these tidings as though silently begging to be assured that this was all some horrible joke. There was no answering smile, and the Pastor knew for the first time that all was not well in his new charge. Having once been awakened to the situation confronting him, he carefully studied each new face and weighed what he heard. His heart became more sick with every passing day as he saw clearly the forces of hostility, the currents of resentment confronting him. Worst of all, he knew that he had not caused these feelings; he had inherited them. Nonetheless they were real and had to be dealt with.

Consequently, the Pastor worked himself almost to exhaustion in the weeks that followed. From morning until late at night he threw all of his energy into getting off to a good start among the people who were now his opportunity to serve his Lord. Time and again, he was bluntly reminded of the fact that his stay was likely to be brief. To be sure there was a sizable portion of·the church's membership that was genuinely glad to have him in their midst, but the fact remained that the Pastor had a hard road to travel, and he knew it.

As the disturbance in him deepened, the questions and doubts began to come. And the biggest question of all was why his Friend had wanted him to leave a happy and prosperous ministry among people who loved him, and to take on a new work among people who obviously did not like him or want him. Every other doubt was insignificant compared to this one. His mind groped for answers. His heart yearned for reassurance, but none came to comfort him. It was then that the Pastor began to know despair that became so deep and dark that it drove him to that solitary stretch of beach on a dreary day when the heavens seemed to cry with him and the moaning of the north wind was like the echo of the sadness and confusion in him. . . .

"Oh, my Master," was his prayer on the beach, "help me, *help* me. Come again to my heart and cause me to know that I am not utterly forsaken."

But again there was nothing. Why was he being tested and tried in such a fashion? What terrible thing in his life, hidden perhaps by pride or covered by self-satisfaction, and thus unknown or at least unnoticed by him, was being purged by this lonely emptiness, this futile yearning and striving?

"Still, O Lord, I know Thou hast come to me at other times. I remember times when Thou has filled me with Thyself. Thou hast come to me in times as dark as this and therefore I *will not* cease to believe or to seek Thee."

Again his tired mind turned to the past. . . .

There was that day when the cold breath of death and destruction blew upon him. He was only a youth at the time. Speeding along the highway, a tire blew out. The car careened wildly, rocking, whipping with screaming rubber from one edge of the road to the other as he fought wildly to bring the hurtling juggernaut under control. There was a mad moment of confused crashing as the car flipped onto its side. The grinding, screeching din of metal sliding on asphalt deafened him as he was flung about helplessly within the automobile. In the midst of it all he cried aloud, "Lord, help me!"

After what seemed to be an eternity of crashing, grating sounds, there was silence. Dimly he realized that it was all over and wondered vaguely if he were dead. Hesitantly he tried to move. There was no difficulty. To be sure, he was crumpled head downward on the floor of the car, but as he explored his condition by moving various parts of his body, it became apparent that he was all in one piece and not seriously injured.

Now he wondered about the condition of the car. Straightening up he was astounded to see that it had come to rest upright on its wheels. Further investigation disclosed that all the paint had been ground off one of its sides where it had skidded on the pavement, but other than that, even the damage to the car was minor. It was a miracle that the vehicle could skid on its side for many feet and then somehow come back to a position on its wheels and he not get a scratch in the wreck.

In that moment it dawned upon him that his wild, desperate cry for help had been heard and heeded. For the first time his Friend became more than a vague mysterious Person, often heard of but never known personally. . . .

"Lord, You were with me then. It was Thy great hand that kept me safe that day. I know now why the miracle that saved me was done. It was because Thou didst have a purpose for my life, a place for me in the work of Thy kingdom."

Again, he thought back across the years to a time his Friend came to him in a glowing experience. . . .

He had gone off to college with a passion for science, especially for delving into the mysteries and magic of chemistry. No intention to ever enter another profession had seriously been considered. Every possible hour he spent in the chemistry laboratory. Then one day a strange thing happened. As he walked along the campus sidewalk, a casual acquaintance, a young man who was a ministerial student, called out to him to come over. With idle curiosity he moved in that direction.

He was greeted with an astounding question. "Say, did

you ever think about becoming a minister?'' When he recovered from the momentary astonishment created by such an obviously ridiculous suggestion, he threw his head back and roared with laughter.

"Me, a preacher? Are you nuts, Johnny?"

"Maybe so. And I don't even know what prompted me to ask the question," came the quiet retort.

As he walked away, the Pastor remembered, he was still shaking with laughter at the most stupid picture that ever had crossed his mind up to that time, the picture of himself standing in a pulpit and preaching.

But the few, simple words that had passed that day during the brief conversation were planted in his mind and heart like a seed is hidden in the earth, there to remain until the irresistible life inherent in it sprang into being when blessed by the sun and the rain. What began as mocking laughter became a serious thought. The thought became concern. The concern became a compulsion, the compulsion became a call to preach.

"No, no! I will not!" he thundered within his heart on the day he knew beyond a question that God was trying to make a preacher of him. "I will *not*. I am going to be a chemist and nothing will stop me."

Nothing? Ah, but God has many hammers to break down walls of resistance. God has plows that can plow even stony hearts and make them fruitful with faith and obedience. There came the time when He plowed the Pastor's heart with tragedy and with pain. When the young man entered the chemistry laboratory that winter afternoon, he had not a care in the world. Even his thoughts about the ministry no longer disturbed him. He had put an end to such nonsense once and for always. He had accomplished it by bludgeoning the thought with contempt each time it came to him. Little did he know of the turning point that would be reached that day. In a matter of minutes all of his carefully maintained defense

99

would be swept away and he would stand helpless before a decision that would determine the course of his life until its end.

The experiment he was conducting that afternoon called for a concentrated form of acid and the proper concentration had to be reached by boiling a commercial type of the ingredient. The odious, brown fumes were rolling up out of the beaker of boiling acid, so he raised a window nearby. As he leaned over the table to pick up a piece of apparatus he expected to use in a moment, someone opened the laboratory door. Instantly a draft whipped through the room. Instinctively the young man drew in a quick breath to shout at the one who had opened the door. Instead of air, he sucked into his throat and lungs the acid fumes that had been drawn in his direction by the sudden draft.

Fiery pain smote him with a sickening blow. He tried to scream, but no sound came. His throat seemed to be in the grip of a great hand. His lungs were aflame with agony. His eyes wept from the acid fumes and the pain. Groping as though in darkness he stumbled to a nearby faucet and with the water on at full force he plunged his face beneath the gushing stream. Quickly he opened his mouth and greedily drank large gulps of water to put out the fire in his throat.

Having gotten all the relief possible by these temporary measures he rushed out to find a doctor. Under the physician's treatment some of the hurt began to wear off until it became bearable. *But he could not speak.* Try as he would, only croaking sounds could be coaxed from the vocal organs. The doctor assured him that even this would be corrected in time and advised a waiting course in order to determine whether the fumes had caused any permanent injury.

Later that day he lay upon his bed recalling the sequence of events that had broken so suddenly upon him. Concern clawed at him now. Would he ever be able to talk again? Would this bring to an end his carefully laid plans for his life's work? As he pondered these things from out of nowhere he heard a voice speak, his own voice shouting in fury — "I am going to be a chemist and *nothing* will stop me."

The sound of his voice was like pealing bells of doom, beating upon his mind and his conscience. Try as he would, in the days that followed, he found no escape from the taunting sound of the words so brashly spoken more than a year before. Although the physical hurt of the injury steadily lessened, another hurt, this one a nameless thing that gnawed somewhere in the innermost recesses of his heart, increased with equal steadiness. At first he slept a great deal, thus finding added relief from the pain. Now, however, he dreaded the nights, for sleep eluded him like a fleeing criminal.

It was during one of those nights when he lay awake staring into the darkness of the room, he became aware of the fact that he was no longer alone. He bolted upright in the bed, alarmed at the knowledge that someone was there in the darkness. He turned on a bedside lamp only to discover that he was alone. "I must have been dreaming," he muttered as he turned off the light and lay down again.

No sooner was the room darkened than he sensed again a presence. This time he *knew* someone was there and though he could not explain it, he knew who it was. There was no surprise in his voice as he whispered, "What is it, Lord?" No audible voice responded and yet he heard with his mind and heart the statement, "If you will speak for Me, you can talk again." That was all his heart heard. And as the moment passed he felt himself alone. Yet, he realized the alternative. If he continued to refuse, he might never speak again.

Even the clarity of the knowledge however, did not settle the issue. Some stubborn streak in his nature prompted him to cling to the idea that it was better to be voiceless and do what he wanted to do than to speak with the tongue of angels in that which he disdained to do. So the time of decision was prolonged and the feeling of dissatisfaction grew more acute and all the while he could only whisper.

Driven to seek some consolation, he went one Sunday evening to church. In the quiet, cool dimness of the sanctuary, soothed by the sound of the splendid voice of the minister, the young man closed his eyes and for the first time in weeks he felt relaxed and at peace. Sitting thus quietly, a picture of himself standing in that pulpit speaking to some audience as the minister was speaking now flashed across the screen of his mind. More than a year before he had seen himself mentally in that position. That time he hooted with derision. This time a strange, deep joy filled his heart. By what miraculous process the transformation in himself had come, he did not know. He only knew that now, all of a sudden, he wanted to stand before people like these and tell them all that was in his heart, just waiting to be told.

Eagerly he sought his room as the services ended. He wanted to settle it all now. To his knees he went, beside the bed. With impatience he began to pray. He was ready to tell the Lord of his decision and of the terms of his surrender. But God tolerates no demands, accepts no terms of surrender from those whom He would use for His glory. What the Pastor did not realize then, but had to learn, was that to be completely yielded the heart must first be completely humble. So he remained on his knees, seeking, until he had been made as an *earthen* vessel to contain the treasure of the Gospel, so that for the rest of his life he would want the glory to be Christ's and not his own.

At long last, when his impatient prayers had ceased, when all conditions had been abandoned, when to the depths he could give himself away, the wondrous Presence was with him once more. Quietly, One came to stand beside his kneeling form. With infinite gentleness a hand was laid upon his quivering heart. Now he could speak and be heard. "Lord," he said, "I want to be Thine. Do with me as Thou vilt for I never *want* to speak again except I speak for Thee."

That night he remained on his knees for a long, long time. Later he slept the deep slumber of one who knows the fullness of peace. . . .

It was hard for the Pastor to pull himself back to the present. He lifted his head wearily from his folded arms, raised his troubled face to the empty, gray heavens and cried, "Lord, Thou didst come to me that night when I gave Thee my life. Since then I have belonged to Thee mind and soul and body. I have sought no greater pleasure than Thy service. Thou hast blessed me and used me to Thy glory in these years. But, Lord, now I feel like a lost child, crying for someone to lead it home."

The words "lost child" stirred chords of memory again. Slowly he began to remember another time when Jesus came in an hour of need. . . .

It was about 5:00 o'clock on the afternoon of March 14th. Although some faint breath of spring had begun to mingle now and again with the icy winds of the long winter, it was still crisply cold. There was a feeling of snow in the air. As the Pastor hurried out of the house to a dinner-meeting at the church, he looked up at thickening clouds. Usually the wild winter made one last slashing onslaught before it retreated in front of the invincible march of spring. Perhaps, he thought, this would be the time for the last heavy snowfall of the season. As he entered his office to pick up some papers, the telephone was ringing. His wife's anxious voice spoke as he lifted the receiver to his ear.

"Do you have Mike with you?" Mike was their first-born, four years old the week before.

"No, I haven't seen him," the Pastor replied. "Isn't he with you?"

"He was in the backyard when you left," the disturbed

voice of his wife continued. "I looked out the window and saw him playing there. About five minutes later I went out to call him in and I can't find him. I thought he might be with you, although I know you have a meeting."

"I am sure he is around somewhere close," the Pastor reassured her. "Call the neighbors and see if he is trying to wheedle a cookie from one of them, like he usually does. And don't be long in getting him home. It's almost dark and I think it is going to snow."

His wife sounded more confident as she told him she would locate the boy and have him home very shortly.

The Pastor did not give the matter a second thought. His son was famous for talking his way into a neighbor's warm kitchen and talking his way out a few minutes later with his chubby hands full of cookies or candy. The neighbors adored him and encouraged him in it, so it was natural to suppose that in a matter of minutes the youngster would show up, full of sweets, and with his brown eyes smiling, say with piping voice, "Mommy, I don't need no supper."

Therefore, the Pastor busied himself with the necessary preparations for the meeting. About ten minutes later the rude jangling of the telephone interrupted his thoughts. He frowned in faint exasperation and said to himself, "What now?" as he picked up the phone.

Again it was his wife. This time real alarm was in her tone. "I have called all the people on this block," she said. "Nobody has seen Mike. I have been up and down the street calling him, but he seems to have disappeared. I don't like to keep you from your meeting, but do you suppose you could come home for a few minutes and help me find him? It is so near to dark, I'm worried about him."

"Sure, Dear, I'll be there in a minute."

As the Pastor drove home he noted that the wind was blowing hard and a few flakes of snow were falling. He headed straight for the backyard where Mike was seen a brief

104

time before. Instantly he saw something that brought quick alarm to him. The gate of the pen where he kept his bird dog, a flashing little setter named Sue, was swinging wide open. Suppose Mike had opened the gate. True, the hook that held the gate closed was too high for the boy to reach, but how else could it have been opened? Beyond a question when the dog was released she had headed straight for the hills that stretched out for miles beyond the house, where she often ran and hunted with the Pastor. Suppose Mike had taken out after her.

He ran to the back door and inquired once more if his wife had any knowledge of the boy's whereabouts. When she said she did not, the Pastor took off at a run toward the hills. In the gathering darkness he could see only a short distance. Added to the difficulty of poor light was the snow that now fell thickly. That combination among the hills made it only remotely possible to find the boy if he had wandered very far. Frantically, the Pastor climbed hills at a run that would have left him panting for breath at other times. Now fear increased his strength to giant proportions and gave him speed. He paid no attention to the rasping of his breath.

Whenever he came to a spot that enabled him to see even for a short distance around him he paused and shouted his son's name. The mocking wind snatched the sound from his lips and hurled it back into his face and he knew that the call carried no more than a few feet at most. Now the snow poured down in a shrouding white blanket, further deadening his shouts. Up the hills he ran, down their slides he plunged, but swifter than his flying feet was the rush of the darkness.

At last, even the Pastor's fearful heart realized that further search was now futile. Standing on the crest of a hill, panting for breath, trembling with exhaustion in every fibre of his body, his eyes wildly trying to probe the gloom, a feeling of utter defeat and helplessness filled him. It was no use. He was too late. The only chance now was to organize a search party, something that would take hours. In his mind's eye he could see the bright-eyed little boy, who was the joy of his heart and his home, huddling behind some rock in the darkness, trying to get out of the wind and the snow that now howled in icy fury. Mentally, he saw that same little form when it was discovered later, all stiff and frozen in death.

A great sob of anguish rent his heart. "O Lord," he cried, "my boy is out here somewhere and I can't find him. He will die out here tonight, Lord. Please lead me to him."

Then came Jesus.

The answer to his prayer was instantaneous. In a moment he felt a great calmness. There was a strange urge to go down the far side of the hill, even though it was now fully dark. Obeying the impulse the Pastor summoned up the last reserves of his strength and plunged recklessly down through the darkness, shouting as he went, "Mike! Mike, where are you?"

Was it the wheezing of his own agonizing breath he heard? He came to an abrupt halt and listened. Faintly he heard it again, an indistinguishable sound that could be the high-pitched voice of his son. Desperately he hunted in the direction from which the sound seemed to come. A few feet further he paused and called again. His heart leaped with joy and relief. It was Mike calling somewhere in the darkness.

"Keep on calling, Son," the Pastor shouted.

The shrill piping voice guided the stumbling feet of the anxious father. In a moment he saw his son, huddled in the scant shelter of a boulder, his little arms pressing the shivering body of the setter dog close to him as they sought to keep each other warm.

"Son, son!" the Pastor wept with joy as he lifted the boy's snow-covered form in his arms. "Oh, Mike, what are you doing out here in the hills at a time like this? Didn't you know you would get lost and might die out here in the blizzard? Why did you do it, Mike?"

106

There was evident surprise at his father's concern in Mike's voice as he answered with the simple directness of a child. "Why, Daddy," he said, "I just wanted to take Sue out for a run like you do."

The Pastor squeezed the tiny form cuddled warm and safe now in his arms. He paused for a moment to thank his Friend. Then parent-like he did a thing that deepened the puzzlement in the boy's mind in regard to the behavior of grownups. He scowled down at his child and said, "Mike, if you ever do a trick like this again I'll give you the worst spanking you ever got."

Mike snuggled his cold little cheeks against his father's neck and sighed and turned his thoughts to more pleasant things — to cookies and a warm bed with a pile of blankets on it. . . .

This time a wan smile lighted the face of the lonely man huddled on the sands of the windswept beach. For a moment his mind was blank. He gazed out over the stormy sea. As far as his eye could see there was an endless stretch of turbulent water. From far out the huge green waves began the final assault upon the beach. As they encountered the shallows they rose still higher as though peering ahead to see what puny obstacle stood in the way to defy them. Then they crested and broke to spill themselves with smothering foam onto the beach.

Watching the restless turmoil of the sea, his spirits lifted momentarily, for words of the Bible came to him —

> They that go down to the sea in ships, that do business in great waters: these see the works of the Lord, and His wonders in the deep. For he commandeth, and raiseth the stormy wind, which lifteth up the waves thereof. They mount up to the heavens, they go down again to the depths: their soul is melted because of trouble. They reel to and fro, and stagger like a drunken man, and are at their wit's end. Then

they cry unto the Lord in their trouble, and he bringeth them out of their distresses. He maketh the storm a calm, so that the waves thereof are still. Then are they glad because they be quiet; so he bringeth them unto their desired haven. Oh that men would praise the Lord for his goodness, and for his wonderful works to the children of men![2]

He reflected upon these words for a moment and then said out loud, "Oh, how great Thou art. Yet I do not have to consider the works of Thy fingers to behold it, for Thou hast written Thy greatness and Thy glory again and again in the story of my life."

Many chapters in that story were in reality not his but accounts of times and ways that Jesus came. Musingly he turned his thoughts once more to a crisis hour when Jesus came. . . .

As the years flowed by, other children had been added to the Pastor's family, four husky, handsome boys and a dainty, delightful girl. One of the few regrets of his ministry was that of necessity he neglected his family. Almost nightly some of the children would ask, "Dad, do you have to go out tonight?" or "Dad, can you be home with us tonight?" Many times he felt he would give almost anything to say *yes* to their doubtful query. When, on all too few occasions, he informed them that he had arranged time to be with them, there were whoops of delight. One night he could not choke back a sob as he heard one of his little ones saying his prayer at bedtime and closing it with this: "And thank You, Lord, for letting Daddy stay home with us tonight."

Even so, his family was an important part of his life. Often he yearned over them in prayer. When anything troubled them or when they were sick, he felt their condition deeply. So, when one day Dave had a rising in his nose that pained him greatly, the Pastor was compassionately concerned for the child's condition. For several days a physician tended the sore place, treating it for a boil. Steadily Dave's condition worsened. A burning fever began to rage in him. It was then that a decision was made to let a specialist look at him. An appointment was quickly arranged and the boy was taken to the famous doctor's office. The skilled healer examined the lad's nose, took x-ray pictures of it, scrutinized them, then called the Pastor and his wife into a private office. For several minutes he paced up and down the room while the anxious couple waited for him to speak. At last the doctor ceased his restless pacing. Then shook his head at some thought known only to himself. Then he turned to the Pastor.

"There is no easy way to say this. You have a mighty sick boy. In fact, it is extremely doubtful that his life can be saved."

"Doctor," the Pastor said aghast after a moment of stunned silence, "you can't be serious! Why, it is nothing but a rising in his nose, isn't it?"

The physician's countenance saddened. "I wish that were the case. No, he has an abcess. It has already eaten away most of the inner structure of his nose. His whole system has been filled with poison from it and there are no glands between his nose and his brain to trap the poison. I am afraid that he will either go into meningitis or into blood poisoning in his entire body. In either case it will likely be fatal and one or the other is almost certain to occur in a matter of hours. I will perform an emergency operation. We will do what we can, but I do not offer you much hope."

As the dreadful words pounded into his ears, the Pastor grew sick in his heart. "Oh, no!" he groaned as the full impact of the physician's opinion smote him. "No, it cannot be!"

The doctor broke in. "I know how you feel, but we must not wait another minute. You get him to the hospital as quickly as you can. My secretary will have made the arrangements to have Dave admitted by the time you arrive, and I will be there to operate. Don't stop for anything. Your boy's life depends upon how quickly we can check this condition. And, Preacher, you had better pray that there is still time.''

Pray he did. He prayed with a depth of intensity not often felt except in crises. He prayed as his boy was put to sleep and wheeled out of the room on a rolling stretcher. He prayed during the long, agonizing minutes that the operation was in progress. He prayed as the still, seemingly lifeless body was brought back to the hospital room.

He stopped praying only when the doctor came in, still clad in the garb of the operating room. "I have done all I can do," he reported with simple directness. "Now, he is in other hands."

The Pastor flashed him a look of deep gratitude as he answered, "Doctor, as far as I am concerned, he has been in those hands from the moment he was born. I gave him to the Lord then. He still belongs to Him now. If He wants to take Dave, it will break my heart, but I shall not protest."

The physician's tired eyes reflected his appreciation in an understanding smile as he turned to leave. But another Physician remained. He stayed with the Pastor and watched beside the silent figure so crumpled upon the bed. The blessed hand that had touched blinded eyes so long ago, that had lifted up the daughter of Jairus and the son of the widow of Nain soothed the raging fever out of the boy and fanned the feeble spark of life until it flamed strong and sure again. The same infinite hand touched the Pastor's heart when fear came and His voice spoke to bring again and again the hush of a wonderful peace. . . .

With the reverie ended, a strong surge of hope laid hold upon the Pastor as he remained quietly immobile on the dreary beach. Speaking to himself he said, " 'Why art thou cast down O my soul? and why art thou disquieted within

110

me? hope in God: for I shall yet praise him, who is the health of my countenance, and my God.'[3] Surely the Lord has not forsaken me. Too many times has He come to share the occasions of need for me to suppose that He has let me down now. Rather I have doubted Him and my unbelief has come between.''

Again looking out at the turbulent sea, words of the Scripture came to mind. ''He that wavereth (believeth not) is like a wave of the sea driven with the wind and tossed.''[4] That is my condition. I have become like those waves out there. And the reason is that I have not trusted Him.''

A great groan of self-reproach and remorse was wrung from the depths of his soul. ''O Master,'' he prayed, ''forgive me. Forgive me.''

Then came Jesus. As He walked the shores of Galilee once and came into the hearts of men, calling them to service, filling them with victorious power for their mission, so He came to the lonely shores of another sea where one who had been called cried for forgiveness and for that same victorious power. Once again a call was confirmed, the victory promised. Now the Pastor was on his feet, his face radiant with joy, his eyes flashing with the familiar flame of determination. He all but shouted his glad response to the coming of the Master. ''Lord, by Thy grace I can do it. They will not run me off. Thou art with me, so I cannot fail. Lord, I am ready to accomplish Thy purpose no matter what the cost.''

No physical eyes could see it, but if the angels were watching they saw a man of God, clad in the whole armor of God, striding along the beach as though eager to do battle. Unseen, too, by human eyes, Another strode at his side. Before these two were finished, a church wept away its coldness and became what it and all of its kind were ever intended to be — ''A shining light in a darkened world.''

[1]Job 23:3a, 8, 9   [3]Psalm 43:5
[2]Psalm 107:23-31   [4]James 1:6

7

THE ALCOHOLIC'S
RETURN

THE VOICE THAT spoke into the telephone, as the Pastor answered its shrill, insistent ringing, was obviously the voice of an intoxicated person. So garbled was the speech that the words were not easily distinguishable at first.

"Who is this speaking?" the Pastor broke in somewhat impatiently. He had often said there were days, when he was called again and again to stop whatever he was doing to answer the clamoring instrument, that he would sell his telephone cheap if anyone wished to buy it. Now to be interrupted, while in the act of preparing a sermon, by someone obviously too drunk to talk with intelligence was just too much.

"This is Malcomb," the bleary voice answered his query.

"Malcomb? I don't believe I know any Malcomb. You must have the wrong number," the minister said as he moved to hang up the phone.

The voice now became more distinct as it took on a shrilling high pitch. "Wait a minute, preacher. You know

112

me. You have seen me many times in the grocery store you patronize."

The Pastor was still impatient. He had been caught in interminable conversations with people who wanted to weep in their cups before, and he did not have time for such a lengthy session now. So he said, "I am sorry, sir, I cannot seem to place you. I am somewhat pushed for time, and I would appreciate it if you would tell me what I can do for you."

The reply almost floored him. "Preacher, I want you to go bird hunting with me."

Ordinarily, the Pastor would have been interested at once. Next to sharing his knowledge of the Word with people, in the pulpit and in personal counseling, he loved to take a good bird dog and roam the fields in quest of quail. He was a crack shot and always kept a flashy bird dog or two. Therefore his company was much sought after by those who desired a hunting companion. However there was one place the Pastor drew the line most definitely and emphatically. It was when it came to hunting with someone who wanted to mix alcohol and gunpowder. So without even a second thought he politely thanked the would-be host and pleaded a schedule that just would not let him get away.

But Malcomb would not be put off. A note of desperation made his voice urgent and pleading now over the wire. It rose to an even higher pitch of hysteria.

"Preacher," he said, "I have a shotgun in my hand right now, and I swear to you if you don't go with me and let me talk to you, I am going out into the woods and blow my brains out. I don't care to live anyhow. And nobody else gives a hoot. I thought that you might be able to give me some reason for living. I figured you, being a preacher, might care enough to see me and talk to me."

By the time the outburst was finished, the words were punctuated by sobbing. As the Pastor listened, he sensed that

113

the threat he heard was not the babbling of a drunk pitying himself. This man meant what he said. He needed help and he needed it promptly and urgently. Yet the Pastor's judgment told him it would be a foolhardy thing to accompany anyone in this condition on a hunting expedition. He countered with, "I do care, Malcomb, and I would like to help you, but it would be much better if you came to my study and talked about your situation there."

Stubbornness made Malcomb's voice cold and bitter. "No, sir," he retorted stiffly, his speech still slurred and garbled by drink. "You either go hunting with me today, right now, in fact, or you'll conduct my funeral. I mean it, preacher." Again the voice broke with weeping, "I can't stand it anymore. I can't stand it. I can't stand it." The frantic words rose to a scream at first and then each time they were repeated they sounded fainter and more distant. The Pastor knew that the man was in the act of hanging up the phone. He shouted in the mouthpiece of the instrument he gripped, "Malcomb, Malcomb! Can you hear me? Don't hang up the phone. *Don't hang up the phone!*"

There was no sound. The instrument seemed dead. Yet there had been no click of the receiver being cradled in its holder and no dial tone buzzed to indicate that the connection had been broken.

Desperately the Pastor tried again, still shouting, "Malcomb! Can you hear me?"

The sound of heavy breathing, accompanied by an occasional snuffing that goes with many tears, told the Pastor that he had an audience again. His voice was deliberately quiet and earnest now. "Listen, Malcomb, I'll go with you. I'll pick you up in about half an hour. However, you must promise me one thing. You must give me your word that you will not take another drink before I get there. Do I have your word on that?"

The response sounded lifeless, hopeless, utterly defeated,

"Yes, Preacher. I'll agree to anything. I just don't care anymore."

The minister obtained Malcomb's address, assured him he would be there as soon as he could change into his hunting clothes and then broke off the connection. True to his word, before even thirty minutes had passed, he pulled up at the address given him and tapped the horn of his car a couple of times to indicate his presence. Pretty soon a tall heavy-shouldered young man came out of the house. He was bareheaded. His dark thick hair, with a slight inclination to being wavy, had obviously not been combed that morning. His handsome face had a surly, drawn look about it. The brown duck cloth jacket was buttoned unevenly. One leather boot was unlaced, with the lacing trailing behind him. He walked with the careful, loose-jointed, high-stepping gait of one too intoxicated to be steady on his feet but determined that no one would become wise to his condition. His blue eyes, the Pastor could see as the youth drew near, looked heavy-lidded and half asleep, obvious signs of the stupor of a drink-fogged brain.

Watching him lurch toward the car, a double-barreled shotgun held slack in his dangling hands, the Pastor knew a double concern. On the one hand, his heart went out to the poor creature staggering toward him, trying without success to appear dignified and sober. On the other hand, he felt concern for his own safety as he eyed the shotgun so carelessly carried. He wondered if he were making the most foolish mistake of his life. He grinned wryly as he thought, *It could be my funeral that will come off rather than the one this fellow has threatened.*

Oh, well, he sighed to himself. *It is said that the angels protect drunk men and fools. This boy is certainly drunk, and I am certainly a fool to go hunting with him. So angels please take note.*

In spite of his misgivings, he cordially greeted the young

115

man who half fell onto the front seat of the automobile with a wheezy grunt. The shotgun bumped the side of the car door and clattered to the floor. The Pastor shuddered in spite of himself, but stuck out his hand and shook the limp one that was extended toward him. "All set, Malcomb?" he asked with forced enthusiasm. "Let's go then. But before we leave town I have one stop to make. It will only take a moment."

Malcomb peered drunkenly at the minister, leered with what was supposed to be a smile, hiccuped and gave a grunt that could have been an assent or an objection. The Pastor neither knew nor cared as he put the car in motion.

The stop that had to be made was at the lunch counter of the nearest drugstore where he had a quart thermos he had brought from home filled with boiling black coffee. Returning to the car where Malcomb sat slouched and half asleep in the front seat, he handed the boy the coffee saying, "Here, Malcomb, get this inside you."

When he saw the slack mouth begin to tighten in protest he added with firmness that would tolerate no foolishness, "Now, Malcomb, don't stall around. You want to go quail hunting. In your condition if a quail flushed in front of you, that shotgun would have four barrels instead of two. If a whole covey flushed, you would see so many birds it would scare you out of your wits. Now drink every bit of this coffee."

Without a word the young man put the bottle of scalding liquid to his lips, flinched as it touched his mouth, then began to sip it. The Pastor had already planned to hunt an area a good distance away to provide as much time as possible to get his companion more sober. As they drove, he insisted that the windows be lowered. By the time the distance was covered, he was half frozen, but the cold air whipping in and the hot, black coffee were having their effect. The young man was steadier on his feet when they pulled into the lane beside the field and got out of the car.

The Pastor could not restrain a shiver of apprehension when he heard the "clunk, clunk" of two brass jacketed shells being inserted into the barrels of the shotgun carried by the half-sober hunter. He released the little blue-ticked white setter from the trunk of the car. She leaped wildly about them for a few moments, barking joyously. At a word from her master, she was off like a white streak, head held high as her keen nose searched the air for the delightful fragrance of quail, her silken tail flashing in a circle as she ran.

Always at such a sight a surge of pride filled the minister. To him the most enjoyable part of the hunt was to see an intelligent, stylish bird dog at work. For a moment he stood watching the little dog bounding away, his dark eyes alight with appreciation. Then still cautious, he positioned Malcomb off to the side of him about fifty feet, warned him to be careful with the gun, and set off at a rapid pace in the direction the little setter had gone.

Before them stretched a long, level field. The soybean crop in which it had been planted had already been harvested, leaving only the stiff, brittle stubble of the bean vines to crackle underfoot. In spite of the half-wary feeling in him, and the fact that he was keeping one eye on his still uncertain companion every moment, he felt a stir of pleasure.

It was a beautiful day. The cold air was heady and sparkling. The fields had on their garb of winter brown. Along the sides of the field were dense growths of dark green pines, their rich tags heavy with spicy fragrance. Across the brown field flashed the little setter on feet that seemed to twinkle, so swiftly did they fly, carrying her trim silky white body like a small floating cloud. Suddenly, with marvelous skill and coordination she slammed to a stop. One moment she seemed to have wings as she whipped across the brittle stubble, the next instant she was a motionless statue of rigid concentration, head up, plumy tail held high, a thing of pulse-quickening beauty.

117

The Pastor's heart bounded with pride. Few thrills that come to a hunter can equal this. There is no tense eagerness, no expectant anticipation that surpasses the moment when the bird hunter moves up, walking lightly on the balls of his feet, body straining, eyes alertly moving, mind frantically guessing at the spot from which the little feathered bombshells will explode.

As Malcomb and the Pastor closed in behind the bird dog, now rigid as though carved of white marble, the grip of excitement drove the last remaining fog of drink from the young man's brain. If his hands shook now it was not from the after effects of his drinking bout. It was gunner's fever. His eyes were clear and dancing. His booted feet, only recently lurching unsteadily, were light and sure as he walked in, gun at the ready.

The dog quivered in every corded muscle as she heard the approaching steps of the hunters. She rolled her eyes trying in vain to locate them without turning her high flung head. The Pastor, watching the dog closer than he studied the ground before her, saw her lithe form crouch ever so slightly. He knew the keen senses of the animal told her the birds were preparing to flush. He called to Malcomb, "Get set. They are coming up."

Even as the words were uttered, the covey exploded into furious flight. The earth seemed to eject the feathered balls of energy. The combined thunder of many powerful little wings thrashing the air made a spontaneous, startling roar. The little dog crouched all the way to the ground, turned for the roar of the guns, glowing eyes glued to the rocketing forms now hurtling toward the sheltering cover of the pines, watching for the first downward plunge of a stricken bird.

For a split second the gunners were paralyzed by the suddenness of the wild flight of the covey. Then instinctively the guns rose. Keen eyes, wide open and glaring in the fever of the moment, sighted briefly along the gleaming barrels.

118

Simultaneously both guns bucked and roared. Just short of the pines, three stricken birds plunged to the earth, clouds of feathers floating down slowly and gracefully after them.

The little setter whimpered with eagerness as she crouched waiting for the command to fetch. At a word from her master, she sprang forward, cast about for a moment, caught the scent of the downed birds, dashed in and picked up one of them. Dangling the bird in her soft, gentle mouth she tossed her head joyfully, proudly. Like one bringing a costly gift to a lover or an oblation to a deity, she pranced gracefully to the Pastor and deposited the form of the bird in his outstretched hand. The caress of the beloved hand was reward and praise enough and made the beautiful little animal tremble with pleasure. Two more times his command sent her out to fetch the birds that had been gunned. When the last of the three dead birds had been tucked into hunting coats, he knelt down and hugged the little setter to him for a moment. She wiggled all over with ecstasy, seeming almost to smile in the delight of triumph and licking his hand with complete adoration.

"Go, girl," the Pastor said as he stood erect once more. "Hi, away." With a bark of gladness she was off again like the wind.

Malcomb, who had silently watched the understanding and love between the man and his dog, shook his head wonderingly and commented with deep respect in his voice, "Preacher, that is *some* bird dog."

For awhile they continued to hunt without a pause. More than an hour passed and several fields had been covered by the steady stride of the hunters. A couple of times the dog had acted as though she scented birds. Cautiously examining every quarter of the breeze before giving it up, she went dashing off again.

Coming at last to the sloping banks of a tidal stream, the Pastor whistled in his dog and said to Malcomb, "This looks like a good place to take a breather. Let's go over beneath that big old pine tree and sit down awhile.''

The younger man consented with a sigh of relief and they strode toward a craggy, wind-blasted pine tree that stood like a giant sentinel, a self-appointed guardian that had established itself on the river bank for the purpose of watching over the endless ebb and flow of the tides that reached up this far from the coast.

Sinking down on the soft, thick carpet of fallen pine tags the Pastor patted the ground beside him once. The little setter instantly lay down on that spot and putting her soft muzzle on one of his outstretched legs, fastened her restless brown eyes on his face in silent worship. Malcomb seated himself near the Pastor and lighting his pipe leaned back on one elbow, gazing out over the river with a moody look in his eyes. The great pine tree sighed its pleasure and took up its whispered talk with the wind. For awhile neither man shared the talkative mood of the tree, each relaxing tired muscles and waiting for the other one to begin the conversation to which this whole morning had been pointing.

After the Pastor had given his young companion time enough to relax and compose himself, he said, ''Malcomb, I guess we both know it's time to talk. You have a story to tell and I have the time and the interest to listen. You have a need. Maybe I have the answer. One thing is for certain, I know where the answer can be found. So just start whenever you will and let it all come out.''

Malcomb glanced up at the Pastor, hesitantly picked up a brown pine tag, chewed it for a moment, broke it between his teeth, spat it out and slowly said, ''I suppose there must be a beginning, but I scarcely remember where it did start, it has been with me so long.''

His voice trailed off and his eyes stared off into space for a moment. Then he continued. ''I reckon it really began with the birth of our first and only child. Marion, my wife, or at least she used to be my wife, Marion and I married young.

120

We had all the hopes and dreams of the very young and deeply in love. Our life together was wonderful at first. I had a good job. Marion was a sweet, devoted wife in every sense of the word, all that a fellow could ask for. So for those first years it was as good as two people could expect it to be. Then, Marion told me a baby was coming into out home and I felt that I had more than my share of the good things of life, so happy was I.''

He took a deep breath and held it for a moment. His fine eyes turned toward the broad shimmering stream flowing silent and strong at their feet, and lingered there, squinting slightly. A sad, pensive expression twisted his handsome face into a grimace of pain. It was with a sigh that he resumed the disclosure of a story so full of mingled joy and sorrow.

"I remember the day I brought Marion and the baby girl home from the hospital. Preacher, I felt like I was walking on air. No man was ever prouder or more deeply grateful for the joy of being a father than I was. Those were the happiest days of my life. But all of that began to change quickly enough. You see, our baby was afflicted. We didn't know it at first. Apparently even the doctors were not aware of it.''

In the shadow of heartbroken memory that darkened the young face, the Pastor saw all of the shattered hopes and dreams that had haunted this boy for so long. Seeing the tears spring to his eyes and knowing the struggle for control that was taking place, the minister prompted encouragingly, "What went wrong, Malcomb?''

His companion brushed away the tears with an impatient hand and answered with a choked voice, "She just didn't grow, Pastor. She just remained a beautiful helpless infant. It seems that some nerve centers or glands or something were injured at her birth. Oh, it was awful to come home day after day and see that nothing had changed. Her soft little body was perfectly formed. She had a beautiful face, golden hair, blue eyes, but she never was anything but a baby. I would

121

hear the fellows at work talking about what their children were doing as they grew up and would think about our poor little Doris and I would have to go away somewhere and cry.

"I have heard people say thoughtlessly that they wished they could keep their baby an infant always, so they would stay soft and warm and cuddly. But they don't know what they are saying. Marion and I would have given anything to have seen Doris change and begin to talk and to run and play." A great tortured sigh welled up from the depths as he said, "She lived for five years just like that — a beautiful, rosy, chubby little angel of a baby."

Malcomb sat upright. Bitterness hardened his face. His tone, as he spoke again, was harsh and gravelly. He bit the words out sharply. "Then she got pneumonia and died.

"Preacher, I got drunk for the first time, the day my little girl died. I heard her little lungs gasping for breath. I watched her struggle, struggle to breathe, and saw her lovely face turn blue and then purple." As he gritted out the words between clinched teeth, his blue eyes were almost black with fury. He clinched one hand into a fist and beat it into the other hand, just pounding, pounding like he was trying to beat back the stealthy steps of the angel of death that he could still hear in the recesses of his mind stalking the life of his baby.

Fiercely he spat words out now. "I put my hand on her little purple face and it was cold, so cold, Preacher. And I cried out to something, to anything, to nothing, 'Give me back my baby. You can't take her from me.' Marion tried to make me hush, to pull me out of the room. I was wild, half crazy, I guess, but for the first time I struck her, Preacher. I turned around and I hit her and I cried out, 'You are not even crying. You don't care that my baby is dead.' Then I ran out of the house, and I got me a bottle, and I gulped it down, and I got drunk, and I was drunk when they buried her."

The words were darts of self-reproach. They hammered one upon the other as they came slowly, grimly, terribly.

"That day," he continued, "I stood by that tiny grave and watched them cover the coffin of my baby. I wanted to see it all so I could remember it. I wanted to see and hear every last bitter part of it because I had made myself two promises. I had promised myself that sometime, somewhere, someway I would get even with whoever had afflicted my child and then snatched her away from me, whether it was God or man, and I had promised myself that I would never again be sober for as much as twenty-four hours."

The angry voice now became flat and listless. Even the flame of fury that had animated it for a time had burned itself out into the ashes of hopelessness. "I have kept the last part of that promise, Preacher. I haven't been sober very often. As to the other promise, I have waited two years for that one to be fulfilled, but it has gotten me nothing. In fact," he added with a scornful laugh that was awful to hear, "I have lost everything.

"My job went first. My wife came to the point she could not stand for me to curse her and beat her anymore, and she left me. My friends turned from me, and I don't blame them. I cursed and abused them, too, because I hated to see them so fortunate and so happy in their snug little world with their fat little brats they boasted about and gloated over. Not one of them could hold a candle to my Doris."

With a mocking smile, intended to indicate nonchalance and complete indifference, he turned to the Pastor and said, "So you see, Preacher, I have nothing. I just don't give a hoot in you-know-where. I can sit here beside you and without one qualm of conscience, stick the barrels of this shotgun in my mouth and laugh as I pull the triggers. I have *nothing*." The matter-of-factness with which he concluded said in effect, "I have had my say. Now you have yours."

The preacher had scarcely moved a muscle, his eyes steadily fixed on the bitter young man during the entire recital. Occasionally his hand had absent-mindedly stroked the sleek head of the bird dog that lay contentedly beside him. For an extended interval the only sound was the sighing of the pine tree over their heads, but deep in his soul the Pastor had been praying to be given words to turn this young man's darkness to the light of God's love and forgiveness.

Then the Pastor spoke, carefully choosing his words and his tones. "Malcomb, you say you do not have anything. But you do. You have a broken heart, an empty soul, a twisted mind and a wasted body. You say you care for nothing anymore. The plain truth is that you care so much and so deeply that you cannot stand yourself the way you have become. You will probably laugh at the suggestion, but I am convinced that beneath all you have said and all you have become, and the Lord knows it is pitiful enough, there still lies something clean and fine and good."

Malcomb's voice was heavy with sarcasm as he broke in, "Thank you, Preacher. Remind me to put a quarter in the collection plate if you ever see me in church."

The Pastor's retort was quick. "Believe it or not, my young friend, I do expect to see you in church, because I know something you will not admit to yourself; your basic trouble is that you have turned against God. He is the One you have been trying to get revenge against. So you have deliberately tried to break all of His laws. You have only broken yourself. You have been trying to hurt Him all this time and you have only hurt yourself and those who love you."

The look of scorn, almost of contempt on the harsh young face did not deter him. His quiet voice went on.

"Yes, I said 'those who love you.' There *are* those who care, boy. They haven't been able to help you because you have been trying to feed your soul on hatred. You have despised those who have tried to love you, your wife, your friends, even your own self, because love did not fit into a promise you so foolishly made to yourself the day your child was buried. Most of all you have despised the love of God."

124

A hoot of derisive laughter interrupted him as Malcomb burst out with a shout, "The *love* of God? How can you say such a thing to me, to *me* of all people? Do you think I am a complete fool? Don't you think I know your loving God could have kept my Doris from being injured when she was born? Your loving God could have made her grow like a normal child if He had wanted to. He could have saved her life if He had cared about her or me or anybody else. Save your sermons for Sunday, Preacher. I am not buying any of that 'loving God' stuff."

The Pastor shook His head in sympathy. He said, "You just won't admit it, will you?"

"Admit what, Preacher? That God, if there is such a thing, loves me?" Malcomb's words had a razor edge of contempt in them.

Then more quietly he added, "Now, tell me truly, Preacher. Can you honestly say to me that any God there may be loves me, when you have heard what happened to my child and to me? Can you honestly say you believe that?"

The pastor's eyes burned into the blue eyes before him. "I *can* say it. I *do* believe it. In fact I *know* it is true."

"Then tell me." Something of the hunger and yearning and frustration sounded in the simple words that were almost a prayer from the young man's lips.

For a moment the Pastor gathered his thoughts. Then with a voice that had in it something of the timeless sighing of the pine tree that shaded them he said, "Malcolm, God knows all about the suffering of your little baby. He understands how your heart was shattered by what happened. You see, because God loves this old world and everyone in it, including you, He sent His Son into the world to save it.

"His Son was a baby, too, Malcomb. Your child was born in a clean white hospital with doctors and nurses hovering around her. His Son was born in a stable with no one but a mother to care for Him. Your child was sheltered and pro-

125

tected from the moment she came into this world. God's Son was hated and hunted from the moment He came into the world. An attempt to murder Him was made while He was still a baby.

"You tell me your Doris was afflicted and frankly I do not know why she was. It could have been an accident or an error. I have no answer for that. But I know it was not by accident or error that God's Son was afflicted. Listen to these words, Malcomb. Hear them well.

> For he shall grow up before him as a tender plant, and as a root out of a dry ground: he hath no form nor comeliness; and when we shall see him, there is no beauty that we should desire him. He is despised and rejected of men; a man of sorrows, and aquainted with grief: and we hid as it were our faces from him; he was despised, and we esteemed him not. Surely he hath borne our griefs and carried our sorrows: yet we did esteem him stricken, smitten of God, and afflicted."[1]

The Pastor paused over the last word, to let it sink in.

> But he was wounded for our transgressions, he was bruised for our iniquities: the chastisement of our peace was upon him; and with his stripes we are healed. All we like sheep have gone astray; we have turned every one to his own way; and the Lord hath laid on him the iniquity of us all. He was oppressed, and he was afflicted, yet he opened not his mouth: he is brought as a lamb to the slaughter, and as a sheep before her shearers is dumb, so he openeth not his mouth. He was taken from prison and from judgment: and who shall declare his generation? for he was cut off out of the land of the living: for the transgression of my people was he stricken. And he made his grave with the wicked, and with the rich in his death; because he had done no violence, neither was any deceit in his mouth.[2]

As the Pastor ended the quotation of the beautiful passage, his youthful companion was sitting motionless, spellbound. Something of the harshness had been erased from his face. A softening, a gentleness had appeared there for the first time. Seeing the first signs of the melting of a stony, barren heart, the Pastor again breathed a prayer for words.

Aloud he said, "Malcomb, you told me of the affliction of your child. I have told you of the affliction of God's Son, and His Son was afflicted because God loves you and all people. You think you have been given a raw deal, that your baby suffered and that you have known a heavy cross and therefore you have decided to take your vengeance against God. But what is your cross of sorrow compared to His? He did not have to suffer. He did not know affliction and sorrow and death because He was weak and helpless as you and I are. He chose that life, He chose that cross. He deliberately gave Himself on that cross so you *could* live, live joyously, victoriously now and live forever with Him. You stood beside the bed of your dying child and hated God, but God turned His back on His Son as *He* died so He could pay for *your* sins, bear your iniquities and your sorrows. And you ask me if I can honestly say I believe God loves you."

In the intensity of his desire to reach the heart of the young man the Pastor leaned forward and his eyes bored into Malcomb's. His words were insistent, demanding, yet gently pleading. "In the light of what I have told you about Jesus, tell me, Malcomb, can you honestly say to me that you do *not* believe that God loves you?"

Malcomb could find no words to utter. His expressive face was working with emotion. Something in him was travailing as if struggling to be born, something fine and clean and good as the Pastor had said, something that yearned to be, but never was until now. It was then that the Pastor's heart began to hammer with joy. His Friend was there! Silently, unheralded He had come. Now, the Pastor thought, now it will happen!

Pressing his appeal home the Pastor continued with new confidence. "And, Malcomb, can you honestly tell me now that deep in your heart, deeper than you have dared to look for a long time, you do not love Him? Oh, son, aren't you tired of making believe that you hate God? Haven't you had enough hurt and heartache without adding this intolerable burden to your soul? Wouldn't you like to have peace and joy again?''

As he paused, he studied the anguished face that confronted him, eager for a decision. The silent pleading, the fathomless hunger, the first breath of new hope and desire that he saw written there were answer enough. Triumphantly the Pastor drove his appeal into the yielding heart. ''Then, son, tell Him you love Him and accept Him. Tell Him, Malcomb, for He is here.''

Gladness, relief, wondering love began to play upon Malcomb's face. With a strangled cry that had in it all the darkness of sin now being forsaken, all the bitterness of hatred now replaced by love, all the striving for forgiveness of a soul too long in shackles and now set free, Malcomb yielded his heart to Christ. His hand clutched blindly at the Pastor's hand, with a mighty grip he clung to it as he wept away the wasted years.

In the glory of those moments the angels sang, the sighing of the old pine tree was a shout of joy, the pastor's heart gave thanks and Malcomb found Christ — and life and love.

True to his expectations, the next Sunday when the Pastor stood before his congregation, he saw Malcomb among the people present. The young man was neatly dressed. Although his countenance was haggard and drawn, there was a shining look of joy on his face and the serenity of peace upon it. With a singing heart, the Pastor preached that morning. When his message had been completed, as always, he gave an invitation for those present to make public their decisions concerning the will of God. The response that came to the invitation was an unforgettable experience for all who witnessed it. Down the aisle came Malcomb, almost running

128

toward the Pastor who stood at the front of the church. His face was wet with tears, but glory lighted his glowing eyes. Again he reached for the Pastor's hand. Finding it and clinging to it, he went to his knees crying brokenly.

Then thrill was added to thrill as the Pastor, sensing a movement among the people, looked up to see a lovely dark-haired young woman coming forward. When she came to the Pastor, her eyes were brimming. She said simply, "I am Marion, Malcomb's wife." With that, she knelt beside her husband, putting her slender arm about his quivering shoulders. Malcomb lifted his face from his hands and looked to see who knelt beside him. His countenance reflected the shock of unbelief, then skeptical hope, then radiant gladness.

"Oh, Marion, Marion my darling," he cried. *"He* has forgiven. Will you forgive me, too?"

She could not speak, but the love in her eyes spoke for her. In his heart, the Pastor spoke for them all — "Thank You, Lord Jesus. O Thank You. Thank You!"

[1]Isaish 53:2-4

[2]Isaiah 53:5-9

8

THE GARDEN WHERE
JESUS WALKED

THE PASTOR GLANCED at the schedule of the afternoon's activities he was holding in his hand. On it was a sizable list of appointments to keep and visits that must be made. He read them off, sighing wearily.

Office appointment - counseling - Mrs. John Blay-
   lock - 1:00 P.M.

Office appointment - Sunday school supt. - 1:45 P.M.

Office appointment - Joseph Randall - 2:30 P.M.

Visits to make:
   Mr. Robert Slade - sick at home
   Miss Nancy Potter - Memorial Hospital
   Mrs. Fred Yates - shut-in
   Grandma Kendrick - at home

The last name on the list held his fancy. That was one visit he looked forward to making. The person involved was the aged mother of one of the church members. Everyone called her grandma. The Pastor had no idea of what her real name

130

was, since he had never heard her spoken of except as Grandma Kendrick. Even so, it was a term of endearment with all who used it because everyone who knew her, he had heard often, loved her. Since she lived some distance from town, she seldom got to church. Although the Pastor had met her and talked with her briefly on occasion, he had not yet had the opportunity of visiting in her home.

Thus it was with a sense of eager anticipation that the Pastor turned his automobile away from the busy streets of the town toward the open country. As he drove, some of the tiredness and tensions of the day began to fall away from him and he relaxed against the seat of the car, drinking in the soft summer beauty of the day.

On either side of the road the lush, fruitful fields streaked away. Forests of corn stood tall and verdant, the stalks nodding tassled heads as though deeply involved in gossip, their rustling blades whispering secrets and the breeze carrying the message from stalk to stalk, row to row, until the entire field was stirred and agitated. In places fields of soybeans lay flat and level, looking like a well-kept lawn so even and uniform in height were the bean vines. In the wheat fields the stalks were golden ripe, waiting patiently for the harvest, heavy-headed like old men sitting idly in the sun, stirring from their lethargy only to bow when some lordly breath of wind swept by on invisible chariots demanding homage.

Groves of pines dotted the countryside; thick forests where trees rudely and ruthlessly crowded and pushed their way toward a place above their neighbors so that they might be the first to catch the gleam of dawning day.

Seeing it all, the Pastor's heart swelled with praise and his lips spoke aloud the words of David's Psalm: "The heavens declare the glory of God; and the firmament sheweth his handiwork. Day unto day uttereth speech, and night unto night sheweth knowledge."[1]

131

But even the beauty of the flowing fields along the way did not prepare him for the breath-taking sight of the little clearing into which he drove at last. The lane into which he turned ambled for several hundred yards among the pines and oaks before suddenly coming to an abrupt end at the open space. Involuntarily, the Pastor braked the car to a halt as he approached the clearing and sat enthralled, almost stunned by the explosion of beauty that came into sight.

The tiny cottage was a picture house, gleaming white in the afternoon sun. It was plain and simple, yet every contour of it was warm and friendly. It seemed to say to the man gazing upon it, "This is a home. No one will be a stranger here. No one need have fear of entering or lingering here." Yet the cottage, with all of its warm loveliness, was like a jewel in a band of gold, for it was encircled by beauty. Patient, loving hands had created artistry in flowers. In beds, in circles, in mounds they clamored for attention and vied for appreciation.

Roses, yellow as the golden sun, pink as the blush on the cheeks of a child, deep red like flaming rubies, pure white like clusters of snow — roses grew everywhere, lavishly giving their fragrance to the summer air. There were beds of stately zinnias, their richly hued heads like jeweled crowns adorning their slender stems. Mounds of fragile petunias displayed their pastel beauty. Peonies, round and white like snowballs, or red like burgundy crowded their prodigal beauty against the driveway. Never had the Pastor seen so many kinds of flowers, so richly colored, so artfully arranged as in the little clearing.

Surely, he thought as his eyes feasted upon all that was before him, *nothing but the hand of God could make this, and surely whoever has planted and cared for this beauty has hold of His hand*.

Almost reluctantly he turned his attention to putting the automobile in motion once more. The sound of the tires on the graveled drive announced his presence and before the car had come fully to a stop, Grandma Kendrick had opened the door of the cottage and was standing on the front porch to greet her visitor. She was a tiny thing, scarcely five feet tall. In spite of the fact that she had lived more than her three score and ten years she gave the impression of youth. Her face was deeply lined and wrinkled by the years she bore, yet when she smiled her welcome, it bloomed with the fresh radiance of a girl. Bright blue eyes, shadowed by suffering and age, still sparkled with eagerness and zest for living. The years had not weighed heavy enough upon her to keep her trim, slender form from being erect and grateful as she moved. The Pastor said to himself as he saw her standing there, *This is the youngest old person I have ever seen, and this lovely old lady just completes the beauty of this place.*

Aloud he said, as he moved toward the house, "Mrs. Kendrick, it must have been in such a place as this that the Lord God walked in the garden in the cool of the day. I have never seen a more beautiful spot."

The sweet old face before him glowed with pleasure as Mrs. Kendrick replied, "I don't know about that, Pastor, but I know that the Lord God walks with me in the garden every day. But listen, Child" — everyone was "child" to her — "please don't call me Mrs. Kendrick. I want you to call me Grandma, just the same as everyone else does."

The pastor grinned and stuck his hand to take the slender one extended toward him. "All right, then, 'Grandma' it is from now on."

"Would you like to come in, Pastor, or could I show you about my garden?" The enthusiastic voice clearly disclosed that her hope was that her guest would desire the latter, which he did.

Together they moved leisurely from place to place in the garden, pausing from time to time while the old lady rattled on contentedly about the kinds of flowers and who had given her this one or that one. To her they seemed to have personalities. She spoke of them as one speaks of friends, telling of problems and difficulties encountered in growing them or sharing the joys and the little triumphs they made possible in her lonely life. The pastor, always appreciative of beautiful things and often wishing that he had the time to plant beauty like this and to nourish it and make it grow, eagerly listened to her clear, sweet voice that went on and on with such evident delight and satisfaction that someone was willing to share these things with her.

When they had completely toured the garden, Grandma Kendrick invited the Pastor to sit with her on a rustic willow bench under the shade of a graceful maple tree. The Pastor glanced at his watch and was startled to see how swiftly the time had passed. "Grandma," he said, "I must be going."

The old lady showed her disappointment. "Pastor, stay a moment longer if you can. Sit here beside me."

For a moment the Pastor could not bring himself to refuse the winsomeness of the gentle old face; so he seated himself at her side.

"Grandma," he said, "I don't believe I ever saw anything as lovely, as homey as this place; the way you have landscaped this clearing, your beautiful little home. But tell me, don't you get mighty lonesome here? I am sure your children are concerned about you living alone in a place as remote as this is. No doubt, anyone of them would be delighted to have you come to live with them for the rest of your life. I don't mean to tamper with personal matters, but it seems to me it is not entirely safe for you to be living alone."

The bright blue eyes that looked steadfastly upon him were snapping with indignation as he began to speak, but in a moment they softened and began to sparkle. With an obvious effort at patience, Grandma Kendrick heard him through.

"Pastor," she replied, "I appreciate your interest and concern. It seems that almost everyone is concerned about me living here all by myself, but I could not leave this place now. It is too much a part of me and I have grown to be too much a part of it. To this house my husband brought me as a bride. Together we cleared this land. Here my children were born and my family grew. It was here my husband died and I wish to die here also.''

She spoke softly, reverently, her wrinkled face made sadly sweet by the flow of memories seen only by her wise, old eyes. Then the frail porcelain-like hand reached out and rested gently and briefly on the minister's hand and she spoke again.

"Pastor, one thing everybody seems to forget — I am *not* alone. You said awhile ago that it must have been such a garden in which the Lord God walked in the cool of the day. Well, He is always here with me. In the day, when I work in my flowers, He is beside me. We talk of many things, He and I. There are rare days when I am sad and I tell Him about my sadness and my burdens, and He tells me He understands. He talks to me and before long the burdens are gone, the sadness has just melted away.

"Many days my heart is full of peace and it nearly bursts with gladness when I see the beauty He created. I just spend the day thanking Him and telling Him how grateful I am that when He made this marvelous world, He decided that He had to put an added touch of His power upon it — something that did not have to be there for practical or material purposes, something that would speak to the soul, something that would say by just being what it is, 'I, your God, love you.' So I thank Him that He made the sky so blue, and the grass so green and the sun so golden. I tell Him I see His love for me in the flowers that did not have to be created in order for this world to be complete from a functional point of view. He just made the flowers as a gift of love, Pastor.

"Then, as if that did not speak clearly enough and as though He wanted everyone to know His love, He put the fragrance in the flower. He made the birds to fly about my garden. I can see why He wanted birds. They do much good in the order of things; they have a practical purpose, but look at that cardinal, Pastor. See it there in the lilac bush? Well, why did He make that bird such a brilliant scarlet and, then, why did He make that bird have in its throat a sweet mellow song like that one is singing now? Do you understand why I spend so many of my days just telling Him of my thankfulness, when on every hand, in everything I can see something that He put there just to say, 'Grandma, this is my gift to *you*. This is to say, *I love you'?*"

Suddenly she grinned wryly and said, "Pastor, I don't talk like this to many people. A lot of folks would probably think old Grandma will soon be ready for an institution if they heard me talk this way." She turned to look squarely into his face and asked with point-blank insistence, "Do you think I am crazy, Pastor?"

The minister's heart was touched. His smile of understanding was enough to express his feelings, but he replied, "No, Grandma. I do not think you are crazy. If you are, then I am too, and I could only wish the whole world would get crazy like that. Seriously, I wish everyone on this earth could see the Lord as clearly as you do and understand His ways through the works of His fingers as much as you do."

Grandma turned again to look upon her beloved garden. She said, "No, Pastor, I am not alone. I spend my days with Him. Then, when the day is gone and the night has fallen, I go into that house and Jesus and I have a wonderful time. I take my Bible and I read His Word. Then I get down on my knees and thank Him again for all the joys and blessings of the day. Many times I ask Him if He isn't ready to let me come home with Him and He says that I must wait a little while longer. I don't mind. I am not afraid. I do not *have* to be afraid. You see, Pastor, every night He tells me that He will stay there and watch over me." The lined old face glowed as she confided these things in a voice hushed with reverent praise.

The Pastor sat spellbound, stirred to the depths of his being. Neither of them broke the silence for long minutes. No words needed to be added. The breeze seemed to bring an extra fragrance from the roses as though it was a tribute to lay at the old lady's feet. The cardinal's flute-like trills sounded a sweet *amen* to what she had said.

Finally Grandma broke the enchantment of the moment. "Pastor, I know you must be going. I have kept you too long as it is, but before you go, would you read to me from the Bible?"

The Pastor was startled at the sound of her voice again, so deep were his thoughts at that instant. He said, "Certainly, Grandma, I will get my Bible from the car."

"No, Pastor," Grandma said, while rising to her feet. "Let me get mine. I would like to show you my Bible and have you read from it, if you do not mind." With that she moved with firm, graceful steps toward the cottage. In a moment she was back, the well-worn Book in her fragile hands.

As he did so often, the Pastor asked, "Is there some passage that is a favorite of yours that you would like for me to read?"

Without hesitation she answered, "Yes, Child. Read to me from Matthew, Chapter 27. You just let the Book fall open. It will open to the place."

And it did, as the Pastor let the old Bible lie loosely in his hand. He glanced down at the pages before him, prepared to read. He was startled. The pages were so yellow, the words so blurred and indistinct that he could scarcely make them out. In surprise he said, "Why, Grandma, I cannot read this print! I can scarcely make out the words. These pages look as though they have been wet."

"They have been wet, Child, many times — wet with my

137

tears," came the simple answer.

The Pastor looked again at the blurred pages. Now he understood. Slowly, brokenly, hesitantly, with deep reverence he read aloud,

> And they stripped him, and put on him a scarlet robe. And when they had platted a crown of thorns, they put it upon his head, and a reed in his right hand: and they bowed the knee before him, and mocked him, saying, Hail, King of the Jews! And they spit upon him, and took the reed, and smote him on the head. And after that they had mocked him, they took the robe off from him, and put his own raiment on him, and led him away to crucify him. And as they came out, they found a man of Cyrene, Simon by name: him they compelled to bear his cross.
>
> And when they were come unto a place called Golgotha, that is to say, a place of a skull, thay gave him vinegar to drink mingled with gall: and when he had tasted thereof, he would not drink. And they crucified him, and parted his garments, casting lots: that it might be fulfilled which was spoken by the prophet, They parted my garments among them, and upon my vesture did they cast lots. And sitting down they watched him there; and set up over his head his accusation written, THIS IS JESUS THE KING OF THE JEWS. Then were there two thieves crucified with him, one on the right hand, and another on the left.
>
> And they that passed by reviled him, wagging their heads, and saying, Thou that destroyest the temple, and buildest it in three days, save thyself. If thou be the Son of God, come down from the cross. Likewise also the chief priests mocking him, with the scribes and elders, said, He saved others; Himself he cannot save. If he be the King of Israel, let him now come down from the cross, and we will believe him. He trusted in God; let him deliver him now, if he will have him: for he said, I am the Son of God. The thieves also, which were crucified with him, cast the same in his teeth. Now from the sixth hour there was darkness over all the land unto the ninth hour. And about the ninth hour Jesus cried with a loud

voice, saying, Eli, Eli, lama sabachthani? that is to say, My God, my God, why hast thou forsaken me? Some of them that stood there, when they heard that, said, This man called for Elias. And straightway one of them ran, and took a sponge, and filled it with vinegar, and put it on a reed, and gave him to drink. The rest said, Let be, let us see whether Elias will come to save him.

Jesus, when he had cried again with a loud voice, yielded up the ghost.[2]

Quietly the Pastor let the Book fall to his lap and lie there still open. Again the worn, yellowed pages were wet — this time with *his* tears. In the hush of that moment there was another rose in Grandma Kendrick's garden, the Rose of Sharon. Another lily shed celestial fragrance — the Lily of the Valley. For the One altogether Lovely had come to share this enchanted, exalted moment with two upon whose grateful hearts the shadow of His cross had fallen.

[1]Psalm 19:1, 2

[2]Matthew 27:28-50

9

IN THE VALLEY OF THE
SHADOW OF DEATH

Ruth sank down wearily in the red leather chair across
from the Pastor's desk. His smile and friendly greeting softened some of the tight lines of hurt that etched her face into a
mask of anxiety. Clearly she was deeply troubled. The agitated hands that clasped and unclasped upon her lap, the
haunting look of fear in her deep brown eyes, the spasmodic
twitching of her thin shoulders all revealed to the minister
that the person before him was barely clinging to the edge of
some precipice of despair that threatened to engulf her. In
every such situation, experience had taught him, the words
he spoke must be carefully chosen, more carefully than his
own understanding might prompt him to select. For a brief
moment he closed his eyes. Perhaps the woman who watched
him marked it down as momentary weariness. But, on the
other hand, she may have guessed that even though that
moment lasted scarcely longer than a heartbeat, he was
silently pleading with his Friend to draw near and speak
through him. If she made such a guess she understood the

note of quiet confidence and assurance as he spoke.

"Whatever it is, Ruth, it is not as hopeless as it may look to you right now. If you would share it with me, I believe we can find some answers together."

The sympathy and concern were enough to break down the last barriers of restraint for her pent-up feelings. The tears began to flow, slowly at first. Then the sobs so long held back by grim determination began to shake her slight form. Wise in the ways of the best of teachers — experience — the minister sat quietly, venturing no further word until the racking sobs grew calmer. Ruth looked up and as she brushed the tears from her face, a slight smile tinged with self-reproach and shame flickered across her features.

"I am sorry, Pastor," she said in a muffled voice. "I promised myself before I came into your study that I would not do this." Her words trailed off apologetically and seemed to hang in a breath of embarrassment.

The Pastor knew that often the best way to get people to talk was simply to listen. As he expected, His continued silence was accepted as an invitation to speak again. Now the words that had come so slowly at first crowded each other and tumbled from her mouth in a nervous hurry.

"It's Ben, Pastor. Something is happening to him. He is changing. So many things are different. I just can't understand it. There is a remoteness, a strangeness about him that I have never seen before. I cannot cope with it. Daily we seem to drift further apart. He seems so aloof, so lonely, and sometimes so desperate. I know he needs me, but he has built a wall about him and I can't get through it. I have tried loving him. And, when that did not reach beyond the shell, I tried scolding him. I guess sometimes I have nagged at him, but, Pastor, he *needs* me, he *needs* me and I can do nothing to help him."

As she paused for a moment, a look of hurt and bewilderment upon her face, the Pastor broke in.

141

"Is he sick?"

"No, he says not."

"Has he gotten into some trouble, with his work or with his relatives?"

"I don't know of any trouble, Pastor."

"Has there been any unusual degree of tension in your home recently?"

"No, Sir."

"Is he working harder? Is he doing too much?"

"Not that I know of. He is on the same job and works the same hours as always."

A fresh flood of tears began to flow. "Oh, Pastor, I know it may sound silly, but somehow I cannot believe it is anything like that. I just have a feeling that something is wrong, terribly wrong. There is a fear that keeps nagging at my mind. I can't put it into words. It's like being in a house and knowing that there is a danger outside. You can't see it or hear it, but you *know* it is there."

No doubt if she had known the danger that did exist, her soul would have been shattered. Surely one of God's mercies is that the enormity of some human tragedy is revealed a little at a time. Neither Ruth nor the Pastor suspected that the months which were just ahead would plumb the very depths of their faith, would bring them to the deepest, darkest valley of all, the valley of the shadow of death. But for the present all they could do was wonder and watch and wait.

Some suggestions were made by the Pastor and they prayed together and parted.

The next Sunday the choir was at its best. The Pastor sat in the chair behind the pulpit desk, his head back, his eyes closed as he listened to the choir. In the very depths of his being the chords of response were stirring. Often he said that there was one verse in the Bible that was a great consolation to him when he tried to sing; the verse that encourages the worshiper to make a joyful noise unto the Lord. He would say, "Now *that* I can do as well as anybody else. All of my efforts to sing are nothing more than noise, but nobody in the world enjoys making such a noise more than I do." So he was stirred in the deep places of his soul as the choir sang that morning.

In the midst of the song, he opened his eyes and let them sweep over the congregation. The people sat spellbound at the beauty of the message pouring from blending voices. He chuckled to himself, "After a number like this one even I can do a fair imitation of preaching."

As the last notes of the song lingered as though reluctant to come to an end, he stood to lead his people in prayer. As always when he prayed he felt a Presence. His prayers were never planned in formal phrases, they were not masterpieces of prose. When he prayed aloud or silently, he was simply talking to a Friend, telling Him his concerns and desires for his beloved flock. Even more than usual the Pastor clung to the hand of his Friend as he prayed that day. And once again He came, this Jesus, and again His train filled the temple and a congregation was caught up in the train of His glory; and hungering, wondering hearts silently proclaimed, "Holy, holy, holy is the Lord God of Hosts."

The prayer was ended. Slowly the people bestirred themselves, opened their eyes and lifted their heads reluctantly. It would not be difficult, the Pastor knew, to lift his audience with his sermon this day. He had chosen to preach on "The Gates of Heaven" that morning. Already it seemed to him as he ended his prayer and looked into the uplifted faces of his people, they had seen those gates standing ajar. In a few minutes he would open his heart to those who waited, but now a voice began to sing from the choir loft behind him.

There was a vibrant richness in the deep bass voice that began softly. It was filled with an inexpressible yearning. At times it sank deeply into pathos, like rumbling thunder. Again it soared in triumphant assurance. It was the voice of

Ben Ross, the young man whose needs the Pastor had discussed with an anxious wife. Surely there seemed to be no disturbance, no emptiness in his heart now as he sang. To the depths the minister thrilled as he heard the golden voice singing,

> If you hasten off to glory
> Linger near the eastern gate
> For I'm coming in the morning
> And you'll not have long to wait.

When the Pastor rose from the chair and took his familiar position behind the pulpit, both hands clasped firmly upon its corners, leaning slightly forward as though to speed his words on their way, he knew his message had begun in the glorious song and all he had to do was take up where the song ended. That morning he *preached*. It was as though he had been filled to completeness and now felt an inner compulsion to pour out the fullness into the hearts of the people before him.

Ordinarily, no thought was in his mind except the sermon that burned in his brain and inflamed his very soul. But now something haunted him even as he preached. Had he imagined it, or was there something very, very real in the words of the song he had just heard — "I'll meet you in the morning, just inside the eastern gate"? It had seemed for a moment that to Ben it was more than a song. Was it a statement of a fact? Was it something that the young man had faced as a present reality? Over and over the words haunted the preacher's mind — "I'll meet you in the morning."

The Pastor was still burdened with his thoughts as he stood at the door of the church and the congregation streamed past him. When Ben, one of the last to leave, came toward him, the preacher noticed that the young man walked slowly. But then he was an easy-going sort of a fellow, he reflected. Suddenly Ben stopped, a look of amazement settled upon his countenance for a moment and then his face twisted in a

144

grimace of sheer agony. Seeing the Pastor looking toward him in evident alarm, he visibly forced his features into an appearance of composure, grinned, and moved forward with a jaunty air, his big hand extended.

The rich voice that could be lifted in such glorious song boomed out, "Well done, Pastor. You really led them to the gates of heaven this morning."

"How about that 'eastern gate'?" the Pastor asked.

"Aw, I guess I just got carried away with my own singing," Ben replied with a shrug of his shoulders.

"Perhaps so, son, and yet —" the Pastor let the word hang in midair. "Ben, I wish you would come by the office very soon. How about tomorrow, on your way home?"

"All right, Pastor. What's up? You have a job for me to do?" the youth asked with a mocking grin.

"Just a few things I would like to talk over with you," came the answer.

As the Pastor walked toward his home he was lost in thought. Even the shouted greeting of children playing in yards along the street, "Hi, Pastor," failed to delight him as usual. The haunting questions were still there. But no answers.

The answers however when they came the next evening were dismaying.

The Pastor opened the conversation. "Ben," he said, "I don't mean to pry, but I would like to know if something is wrong. I saw the way you walked yesterday. I heard something in your voice when you were singing. Tell me, is something the matter? What caused that pain that struck you yesterday when you were leaving the church?"

Ben made his face expressionless. Only the pleasant grey eyes filled with quick alarm betrayed the fact that the Pastor's words were probing into carefully concealed truth.

"What is it, Ben? You know you can trust me with any confidence. Whatever it is, maybe I can help," the Pastor

145

continued gently.

The young man closed his eyes in weary resignation. He took a deep breath and held it so long it sounded like a small explosion when he released it. He shuddered. His face grew ashen and he looked sick.

When he spoke, it seemed that he had to drag the words out of his own mouth.

"Pastor, no one knows what I am going to tell you but my physician and myself. I have thought of coming to you before and asking you to pray with me and for me, but I just put it off. You see, I have something wrong with my hip. It started months ago. At first I paid no attention to it, marked it down in my mind as a sprain or something. I figured it would soon wear off. But it hasn't. It has gotten steadily worse.

"After a while I couldn't stand the hurting, so I went to a doctor. I didn't tell anyone else about it. Somehow it seems silly to complain about a pain in the hip. Nothing definite has been revealed yet. The thing is that it catches me now and then and I can't seem to move. The pain is so terrible when it comes I have to bite my tongue to keep from screaming. If something isn't done soon, I'll go out of my mind. I can't hide it much longer. I try to keep it from Ruth, and have kept it from her so far, but she knows something is wrong.

"Pastor, what can I do? I don't want her to know, and yet I can see that it is breaking Ruth to pieces not knowing what is happening to me. Please tell me what to do. I have come to the end of my endurance."

"Ben," the Pastor said, "I don't need to tell you what to do. You know already. I am not just handing you some pious platitudes when I tell you the Lord God is the Great Physician. Maybe this doctor doesn't know the cause of your trouble, but God does and He can give your physician the knowledge to discover it, too. Do you remember what God told Moses at the burning bush? Moses stood there arguing with God, telling Him about his physical handicaps and

146

troubles. He said, 'Lord, I can't do this thing You tell me to do. I can't talk like other men.' And God answered him, 'Who hath made man's mouth? or who maketh the dumb, or deaf, or the seeing, or the blind? have not I the Lord?'[1]

"I offer you no false hope, Ben. I do not know the cause of your pain. I do not even say it can or will be cured. I only want you to know that you are held in the hollow of His infinite hand and that He has promised 'As thy days, so shall thy strength be.' "[2]

Dark shadows of fear crept into the intense young eyes. "But, Pastor, suppose it is something serious and suppose it is not God's will that I be healed." A note of horror had come into his voice.

The Pastor knew the thoughts tearing at the young man's mind, the fears that were cutting his heart. What could he say? What comfort could he give? The right words would ease the agony of doubt. The wrong words would bring midnight to an anxious soul.

"Ben, it is no joke with me when I say to you, in that case, 'I'll meet you just inside the eastern gate.' "

Neither of them could say more, so full of emotion were their hearts in that moment. However, two strong hands met in a fervent clasp of understanding, and in that moment each of them knew that they had made an appointment in eternity.

Days slipped away in busy succession. Neither of the men felt the need to discuss Ben's condition again. Whenever they met, the Pastor's compassionate eyes searched the young man's face for signs of need. Sometimes he looked so long and searchingly upon him that Ben instinctively knew that a silent question had been addressed to him — "Ben, do you need anything? Can I help you in any way?" Usually there was a wan smile or a quick grin that would say with a soundless voice, "I'm all right, Pastor. I will let you know when I need you." And so the minister would turn away, still anxious but satisfied.

147

The lazy summer days went by with deceptive speed. The gay tinge of autumn began to blend with the golden ripeness of mellow summer, shyly at first like little girls with gay colored shoes on sun browned feet, half afraid to call attention to them and yet so anxious for them to be seen. Thus did the summer display the russet that darkened the shrubs and the flecks of vermillion and gold that suddenly appeared on the leaves. A sense of expectancy and eagerness like the thoughts and emotions of lovers about to meet seemed to pervade the flowing tide of life in the changing season.

These were days which the Pastor loved. Autumn was his favorite season. It always seemed to match the sweet nostalgia of the restless depths in him. It was then that a heart made sensitive by the sorrows and tears of so many people yearned more fervently, felt a greater compulsion to love and care for his people. Perhaps it was the inexorable invasion of approaching winter that stirred him to deeper compassion, like the old warrior of the Cross, Paul of Tarsus, reaching out with his heart to Timothy and urging, "Do thy diligence to come before winter."[3] Whatever it was, the Pastor thought more longingly on the condition of his young friend during those autumn days. It could be that somehow he knew, even though there were no perceptible signs of his condition, that it was turning to autumn in Ben's life, too.

There was a shock of disappointment and deeply personal sorrow the day Ben came again to the Pastor's study and told him that he was being transferred to another city. It meant a promotion for him, he confided in the Pastor, and he could not pass up the chance to go up in the organization in which he expected to invest the remainder of his life.

"Besides," he said, "I believe it will be good for Ruth and me to go to another city and start again. She still does not know anything except that I have an occasional pain in my hip. I cannot always hide the fact from her when it catches me. Perhaps you have noticed, Pastor, how tired she has become. It is because she is worrying about me. It would not be fair to tell her more than she already knows, and my silence irritates her and her persistent worrying aggravates me. So we are going to move to a new city, and we will try to get a fresh start.''

The Pastor's eyes were downcast for a moment, to hide his personal dismay at this turn of events. This splendid young man had become so close to him that he felt toward him as a son. When he spoke it was with forced heartiness. "Ben, I am glad for you. I knew you were sure to get a break like this some time soon. You have too much to offer to have your talents hidden for long. Sooner or later someone with authority in your organization was bound to discover you and give you the larger chance you so well deserve. Needless to say, I wish you could stay with us, but since you cannot, God bless you and keep you, boy. You will always be in my prayers.''

Again Ben took the Pastor's hand in his own and pressed it with a clasp of warm gratitude. For a moment he continued to grip the hand of the man who was not only his pastor but also his friend and he said, "Thanks for everything, Pastor. Thanks for everything.''

He turned away quickly and started out of the door. On the threshold he suddenly stopped and again faced the minister, still sitting quietly at his desk.

"Pastor, if I should not see you again, remember I'll meet you in the morning just inside the eastern gate.''

He did not pause long enough as he departed to see the smile on the pastor's face or the quick start of the tears in his eyes.

Occasionally word came from the distant city with news of Ben's progress and of his condition. Sure enough, the two of them had made a new start and were deeply happy. The change had even seemed to relieve much of Ben's pain. The Pastor was greatly encouraged to hear these things about two of his favorite people.

Then one day when winter was trying its best to break down the last defenses of the fall and force the long deep sleep upon the earth and its creatures, there came a message that made the Pastor feel as though the snow-laden wind that swirled out of the north had locked his heart in its icy grip. When he answered the telephone on his desk a voice so muffled that he did not recognize it spoke his name. Then he knew.

"This is Ruth," the voice continued. "I am calling about Ben."

For a moment she could say no more and only the sound of hopeless weeping reached the Pastor's ear.

"Please, Ruth," he said. "Get hold of yourself. Tell me what has happened."

He heard a long shuddering sigh as the weeping was forced under control. When Ruth spoke again every word was forced like a hammer beating the Pastor's brain.

"Ben has cancer, Pastor. The pain began to increase a short time ago and finally Ben told me what I had suspected for a long time even though he tried to keep it from me. Recently he came home one day from the office in agony. I knew something was wrong when he left his job so early. He has been working so hard. He wouldn't tell me at first how badly he hurt, but soon he was groaning with pain and rolling back and forth on the bed. I called a doctor. He gave Ben a shot to ease the pain and told him to be at his office the next day. Ben went to the hospital for tests." The strangled voice turned into weeping again for a few moments. How helpless the Pastor felt! At last he heard the sound of deeply inhaled breath, and as it was released a sobbing cry accompanied, "Oh God, oh God, what can I *do?*"

"Ruth," the pastor admonished, "you must hold on to yourself. Please tell me the rest of it."

"I am sorry, Pastor. It's just that I have been keeping this inside of me for so long and trying so hard to keep my chin

150

up. Well," she continued, "as I said, they made these tests and they found that Ben has a cancer that began in his hip and now has spread."

Again the cutting edge of hysteria knifed into her words — "They don't give him any hope. They are going to operate, but there isn't a chance in a thousand that it will do any good."

For a while the Pastor listened as Ruth gave additional facts as best she knew them, filling in details occasionally as the minister asked questions. His own heart almost overcome with sadness, he told Ruth that he would be on his knees before God at the hour of Ben's operation. As it had ever done, the quiet assurance in the Pastor's words gave Ruth the courage she needed to keep on praying — and hoping.

Many times each day the Pastor talked of the needs of his human friend with his divine Friend. At such times he gave fervent thanks that he had such a Friend, and that his Friend was the Shepherd of the undershepherd, that as a pastor he, too, had a Pastor.

His life as a minister was in many ways a lonely one. In the very first pastorate he had learned that close friends were a pleasure he could not afford. He soon learned that there are always people in the church membership who were quick to criticize and condemn if any minister paid more attention to some of his flock than to the others. The years had made him, like his Lord, a man of sorrows and acquainted with grief. He sometimes felt that his ministry was an island of compassion and love in an ocean of sorrow and suffering, his understanding and sympathy an oasis of relief in a wilderness of broken hearts, shattered hopes and ruined dreams. Every day he emptied himself into the needs of his people and he would have it no other way. Yet so much of it had to remain forever sealed within him for most of the deep things shared with him by his people had been and could be shared with no one else.

So the Pastor was grateful for his Pastor, the One with

whom he shared all things in prayer, the One who provided a constant flow of strength and faith and love into him so that no matter how frequently or completely he must empty himself into the lives of others, be it day or night when the occasion arose, there would be more for him to give.

Sometimes then, it was with desperate urgency that he prayed for the young man he had come to love as one of his own. Daily he longed to be with him, to offer some word of comfort and strength, to share the horror of the disease that was cutting the very roots of life itself. But all he could do was pray.

And there came the day that the Pastor had long expected. Late that night, Ruth called from the distant city. Her message was tragically brief. "Pastor, Ben is nearing the end. He wanted me to call to ask if he could see you once more before he goes."

The Pastor choked back the sorrow that made a knot in his throat so big that for a few moments no words could come. Quietly, sadly, he replied, "Tell him I will be there tomorrow, Ruth. Tell him to hold on, 'til I arrive."

The next day was bitterly cold. Overnight a blanket of snow had fallen. In spots the highways were glazed with hard packed snow that made them treacherously slippery. It was a mean day for a long journey. As the Pastor drove, the tension in him mounted. His nerves were taut. The irritation in him increased hourly. He knew he was racing the dark angel of death. And it seemed that he was bound to lose because of the slowness at which he must travel. The journey seemed endless, but at last it was over.

At the hospital, Ruth was awaiting him. When the Pastor saw her, his heart reached out to her in a rush of compassion. Her face, always thin, now was drawn with suffering. Her eyes had the haunted look of one who had looked too long and too helplessly upon the pain of a loved one. The half circles of the purple shadows of strain etched and lined her deeply set eyes and told of the depths of her unspoken sorrow. She was so close to the breaking point that every movement of her body had a jerky, feverish intensity about it.

As the Pastor took both her cold hands in his he asked hesitantly, "Is he — is he still living?"

The voice was almost a croak. "Yes, poor thing, he is still alive. He has been asking for you all day."

"Will he know me when I go to him?"

"Yes, Pastor, he is conscious most of the time." A look of unspeakable pride lighted her eyes. "Do you know, all through the day he has refused to take anything to make him sleep or deaden the pain. He wants to be conscious and rational when he sees you."

"Bless his heart," the Pastor murmured. "Let me go to him now so he can soon get a shot for the agony that must surely be upon him."

He recoiled momentarily with horror when he opened the door to Ben's hospital room. So wasted was the figure upon the bed, so yellow and shrunken the face that it looked as though a mummy lay prostrate there. Before the dying man opened his already vacant eyes, the Pastor had taken hold of himself with an iron hand so that when he called out, his voice boomed with confidence and joviality.

"Ben, you rascal, are you going to sleep all day? I drive all day to get to see you and here you are acting like a gentleman of leisure with not a thing to do but eat and sleep and be waited on hand and foot."

Quickly Ben opened his eyes. For a moment they moved desperately around the room as though the place was unknown to him. Then they came to rest upon the familiar form of the man who was once his pastor and still his friend.

He struggled to raise his head from the pillow. In an eerie whisper, he said, "Pastor, I'm glad you got here in time."

"What do you mean 'in time'?" The grin on the Pastor's

153

face was obviously forced. "You have plenty of time. Why, I wouldn't be surprised to see you get up and walk out of here before long." He tried to make the words sound genuine, but he understood that Ben would never walk out of the hospital room or anywhere else.

"Thanks, Pastor," said Ben with a wan smile. "You know and I know that time has run out for me. Let's not waste any of it, please. There is much to say and so little time and strength to say it."

His head sank to the pillow. His breath came in gasps. A low moan of pain broke his cracked lips. The yellow face twisted in an agony and as the hurting mounted his entire form writhed in the grip of its torture. The moan became a scream. The long frail hand that a moment ago lay in the Pastor's hand weak and helpless now gripped like a vise. Through gritting teeth the cracked voice sounded — "I can't *stand* it. I can't, I can't!"

After what seemed an eternity the spasm of pain wore off momentarily. Again Ben made an effort to speak, his words so low the Pastor had to lean close to catch them. "Pastor, in spite of all that has come to pass, these have been wonderful days. For one thing, Ruth and I have been so close. You remember I once told you we had become as strangers. We found each other again, Pastor. The love that has grown between us has become a sacred thing. I thought we loved each other before, but it was never like this.

"But something more wonderful than that has happened since I have had this thing in me. Oh, Christ has been so real, so close, so good to me. Pastor, He has been here. He has never left me for a moment. I have never felt anything like the joy and peace that has filled my heart during these last few weeks. Oh Pastor, now all I want, all I can think of is how good it will be to be with Him forever."

As the Pastor stroked the feeble hand that he held in one of his, he was quietly weeping.

"Ben," he began, but the whispery voice interrupted.

"Let me finish, Pastor. I need to tell you these things because I want you to know I am all right. There is not a shadow between. I have done all that needs to be done before I go away. Yesterday the children were here, and I told them all that was in my heart to say to them. They know I will be going soon. I told them about how good, how beautiful my Saviour is and that I am going to live with Him and I will be waiting for them to come live with us there also. They cried a little, but they know where I will be and they promised to meet me there someday. Ruth and I have talked many times. We have gone deep, dear friend. Ruth will be all right, too. You may have to help her a little, but she will make it because she has found Him, too."

The voice was almost gone. The weary, pain-filled eyes were becoming glazed. The breathing was more of a gasping than ever.

"Please, Ben," the Pastor begged, "don't try to talk anymore. Let me call the nurse and have her give you something to make you easy. You don't have to tell me any more."

The parched lips formed the word "no" but no sound came. With a great effort Ben raised his hand in protest. Then he beckoned for the Pastor to lean closer. When he was near enough to reach, the dying man pulled him down until his ear was almost touching the blue-tinged lips. "I'll meet you in the morning, just inside the eastern gate."

That was the last thing the Pastor heard from the lips of his friend. After that he sank into a coma from which he never aroused. When it was all over, the Pastor took the hand of the widow as they stood beside the fresh grave and said, "Ruth, we have an appointment — just inside the eastern gate." They both know it is an appointment they will keep.

[1]Exodus 4:11
[2]Deuteronomy 33:25 [3]II Timothy 4:21

10

A STUBBORN
HEART YIELDS

Good morning, Mrs. Travis," the Pastor said as he paused in the door of the hospital room.

The woman to whom he spoke looked up. A quick warm smile of welcome lighted her dark eyes.

"Why, Pastor, how nice to see you," she replied.

Thus began one of those wonderful times when Jesus came and by His transforming presence changed a life utterly and completely. It never crossed the Pastor's mind as he went about the routine hospital visitation which he had marked out for the day, that he would have the opportunity to introduce his Friend to someone who needed Him so desperately and who had fought against admitting it for so long. In the plan of God for surrendered lives there are constantly those surprising opportunities to witness and to help.

Often the Pastor reminded his congregation that a Christian should consider himself to be operating under sealed orders for each day; that every day should be filled with a sense of expectancy that God will do wonderful things.

Perhaps to many who heard him at such times, his words held little meaning; but he knew whereof he spoke. More times than memory could recall he had been confronted by doors of opportunity suddenly opening. Scarcely did a day ever pass that did not hold some surprise of joy in beholding or sharing the unsearchable riches of Christ.

But on this particular day he anticipated no such experience, because the work he planned to do was so routine. Of course there was always the knowledge of the Saviour's presence in times and places of need. Never did he stand beside a hospital bed, such as now, that he did not know in the depths of his soul that the Great Physician stood beside him.

Even though he realized that the woman before him was a devoted Christian, it was as natural as breathing to talk to her about the goodness of God.

"Oh, Pastor," she said, "how well do I know it. When I was a girl thirteen years old I met Jesus and I put my hand in His. It has never been withdrawn from that moment to this. I could never tell you the joy I have known walking at His side. For more than fifty years He has held me in the hollow of His blessed hand, and I know He is holding me now."

With a radiant face and a joy that sometimes spilled over in tears of gratitude, Mrs. Travis went on to tell the Pastor of the faithful years of dedicated living. She told him how she had begun to serve Christ in a small country church in South Carolina, working with young people. Then the time came when her husband was transferred to another place to work.

She said, "That last Sunday I told my group of young people that I was leaving. And I told them that the deepest hope of my heart was that I had been used to bring at least one of them to my Lord."

She paused for a moment as though living again that sacred hour and as she remembered, the fountain of joy was too great to be contained in her heart, and it spilled over in the tears that slipped down her gentle face.

"And then," she continued, "I had one of the happiest moments of my life, Pastor. Not one but *five* of those girls came and crowded around me. Some of them put their arms about me and some of them just held my hands. But they all said, 'Mrs. Travis, you made Christ real to me!' Since then, Pastor, even though I have never been back to that church, many of those girls, married now and with families of their own, have written me that they are trying to teach their children in the ways of Christ as I once taught them."

The wrinkled hands were clasped in ecstasy upon the sheet that covered her slight form. The tears flowed freely.

"God has been so good — so good — so good." It was an anthem of praise from the aged lips.

There are times when a minister is not the giver of blessings but the recipient. This was surely one of those times for the Pastor. Perhaps, too, this was in the plan of God as a preparation for the wonderful experience that was to follow. Certainly, after listening to such a testimony, the Pastor felt in himself a deeper joy, a firmer faith.

Just then a nurse came briskly into the room, her starched, immaculate uniform rustling as she moved. In her hand was a tray with the usual assortment of paper cups containing the usual assortment of medicine.

"Mrs. Travis," she spoke with a cheery voice, "here is that pill-pusher again."

Then noticing the fresh tears upon her patient's face she cast a look of reproach at the Pastor and her voice almost crackled with sternness as she asked the woman, "Are you all right? Is anything disturbing you?"

The Pastor, realizing that he was about to become the center of a storm, started to interrupt with an explanation. However, before he could speak, a smile like the sun finding an opening in the rain clouds lighted the sick woman's face.

"No, child," she said, "I am all right. I was just sharing

with my Pastor some of the good things God has done for me. These are tears of gratitude you see.''

"Oh," the nurse said with relief. Then turning to the pastor she added crisply, "I wish you could do something for that old man across the hall.''

"Perhaps I can," the minister replied quickly. "I will try."

The young woman sighed resignedly. "No, you can't do anything with him. He won't let anyone help him. Another minister was in there a few minutes ago and the old man raised such a row he had to leave. That man is over seventy years old, and he is facing a serious operation in the morning. The chances are he will not even survive the operation, but do you think he is concerned? Do you think he will let anybody talk to him? Oh, no! As I said, he just chased a preacher out of his room not fifteen minutes ago. Don't waste your time trying to talk to *that* man."

"Tell me who he is," the Pastor requested.

"All right. But don't say I didn't warn you — this time he will really be wound up if a preacher so much as sticks his head in the door."

Seeing that her objections were accomplishing nothing, she said, "His name is Norville Graham."

As she turned away, the nurse grinned and quipped, "If I see you running down the hall with that old man chasing you, I'll open the door for you."

The Pastor chuckled as in his mind he saw himself being chased down the hall. Mrs. Travis laughed merrily at the thought.

Then soberly he said, "Mrs. Travis, we know what that fellow needs, don't we? I am going to try to reach him. Will you be praying for me constantly while I'm in that room?"

"You know I will, Pastor. And we know what will happen if that man opens his heart to Christ. Yes, I'll pray. You go to him now. He needs you."

159

The Pastor left the room, but before he knocked at the door across the hall, he walked along the corridor, asking guidance and help in the mission awaiting him. Coming to a window at the end of the hallway, he stood looking out for a long moment, then lifted his face to the blue of the sky and whispered, "Oh Lord Jesus, go with me into that room. Speak through me. Touch this heart that is so hardened against Thee, and melt it with Thy loving presence."

Reassured now he tapped upon the door. A tall, stately woman opened it in response to his knock. She stepped into the hall and closed the door. Her taut features spoke of anxiety and grief. Her greeting sounded hollow as she simply said, "Yes?"

The Pastor introduced himself and said he had come to speak to Mr. Graham. A quick look of alarm slipped into the woman's eyes. She told him that she was Mrs. Graham and then added apologetically, "I don't know what to tell you. My minister was here awhile ago and my husband got very upset when he tried to talk to him." A sob caught at her throat and her lips quivered briefly. "I am so ashamed of the things he said and the way he talked to my minister." Gaining control of herself she added, "It might be better if you waited until another time to see him. He is still mumbling and fussing because I let my pastor come in."

"Well, Mrs. Graham," the Pastor replied, "I will not intrude if you think it best to come again, but a nurse told me your husband is facing a serious operation. Later might be too late."

"I know it, I know it." The woman began to cry. "He needs someone."

The Pastor spoke compassionately. "I tell you what; let me just speak to him. If he resents my presence or begins to get too upset, I will take no offense, and I will leave. But let me try."

With resignation and obvious misgiving she acquiesced

and opened the door. As the Pastor crossed the room he studied the figure lying upon the bed. He noticed first the shock of white hair. It was like a snowy lion's mane above the craggy, deeply lined face. Fierce dark eyes glowered from beneath bushy brows. The wide sensitive mouth was grimly closed and made the jutting chin look all the more rock-like. The whole mien was one of determination, stubbornness and ferocity.

Approaching with a smile, the Pastor introduced himself.

"What?" The voice suited the face of the man who almost roared the word. "Another blasted preacher? I just sent one packing!" The fierce eyes opened wide and the pupils rolled upward as though in a mute appeal to heaven for patience. The voice grated on, "Why can't you fellows mind your own business?"

If he expected that the outburst would startle his visitor and humble him, there was a surprise awaiting. Like a whiplash, the Pastor's voice crackled. "I am minding my business, sir. It just happens that my business is trying to help people, even stubborn ones like you."

Surprise appeared in the glowering eyes and a grudging look of respect was there briefly.

"Well," Graham growled, "you *are* a determined cuss, aren't you?"

"Just as determined as you are, sir."

"Now listen, son," a flicker of warmth came into the rough voice for the first time. "I'll have you to understand that better men than you have talked to me about religion. None of them got very far." He seemed pleased with the sound of this last remark, but the Pastor knew he had at least won an opportunity to speak.

The Pastor responded to the softening in the man before him. He said, "Maybe they didn't get very far, but the thing that concerns me is that before much longer you are going a long, long ways."

161

"You can't scare me," the old belligerence was back. "I have a lot of good years before me, I'll have you know."

"I hope so," the Pastor answered, "but I know how they could be better years, whatever may be their number."

A soft chuckle rumbled up from the sick man. "I can read you fellows like a book. I know exactly what you are going to say. Like that other preacher fellow who was here, you are going to say, 'Go to church, go to church.'" Sarcasm dripped from the mimicry.

"Well, sonny," he continued, "I *do* go to church. I have been a member of a Sunday school class for forty-one years, and I haven't missed more Sundays than most folks do. But do you think I am going to join that church? No sir, I know too much about too many of the pious hypocrites who warm the pews Sunday after Sunday — I see them on Monday, mister. I know what they do — they put on a long, pious face and say 'Good morning, dear brother' when they see me at church. They ooze with unction. But blast their bones, they would cut my throat on Monday, and I know it, and they know I know it. Ha! Don't talk to me about joining up with a bunch of sour-pussed, long-faced, pussyfooting, back-slapping hypocrites like that. And furthermore" — the outraged voice was almost breathless now — "and furthermore, if I didn't respect the cloth I would put it in a lot stronger language than that!"

On and on the voice droned and grumbled, accusing, condemning, complaining. When at last he had poured out all of his vehemence, his mouth clamped shut like a steel trap closing.

In spite of himself the Pastor had to laugh. "Say, who *is* the preacher here?" The only answer was a disgusted snort.

Then soberly, the Pastor said, "Mr. Graham, let me ask you just one question, and I want an honest answer. You say you have been attending a Sunday school class for forty-one years. In that time, you have heard more about Jesus Christ than anyone else. You must have heard a thousand lessons taught about Him. It is inconceivable that you have listened to all of those words and not come to know something about Him. Now tell me, sir, in those forty-one years, what fault have you come to see in my Saviour? Tell me how *He* comes short or how *He* has failed in any way to live up to your expectations, if you have had any.''

A look of astonishment twisted the face before him. The fierce old eyes blinked rapidly in surprise. ''Wh-hat do you mean?'' he gasped.

''I did not come to talk about joining a church,'' the Pastor resumed. ''That is not the step you need to take.'' Something warm and vibrant had come into his voice now. ''Sir, I want you to know my Saviour. All of these years you have mentioned, you have heard of Him and you can point out no flaw or failure in Him. He lacks nothing that you need. Deny, if you can, that your heart has hungered for Him.''

He paused as his eyes searched the countenance before him. ''I can tell by the look on your face that what I say is true. All of this time that you have let slip away from you, there has been no real joy in your life, no real peace in your soul. Your blustering, your talk about the hypocrites and all the rest, has been to justify yourself in turning Him away from your heart. And all of these years He has come back again and again.

''And He is still waiting. *But how long, how much longer can you wait?* Has it been so long you cannot open the door to your heart even to One who loves you as He does?''

The impassioned words were like hammer blows upon the old man's stubborn heart. His breath grew short. His eyes dilated and seemed to protrude. And yet it was not the Pastor's appeal that was breaking down the barriers. Oh, no! *Someone else was there.* To that bedside, to that hungry heart, came Jesus. The Good Shepherd had heard the first faint cry of the lost sheep. The Father had seen the first signs of the weary plodding feet of the prodigal turning homeward. The Mighty God had noted the tears of penitence in a melting heart long before they reached the eyes. In all of His glory, His love, His mercy, *He was there* — almost they could see Him. Almost the veil was drawn back so they could touch Him.

Caught up in the rapture of that Presence none of the three people in that room could move. There was a breathless silence. Then a terrible groan was wrenched from the old man's lips. "O-o-o Christ — O-o-o God; do You still love *me?* After all I have done? Will you save *my* soul?"

Never had the Pastor heard more pain, more longing put into words than in that moment. He kept silent, for he knew that this was no time for human intrusion. In this fragile moment stubbornness was dropping from a yielding heart like dried leaves, blown away by the breath of God. The door, so long closed, was swinging open at last. Because he, too, had passed through this experience he knew that in this sacred moment the hands that made the universe, the hands that were scarred by the cross were touching with infinite tenderness and power, a heart and soul and mind and will and creating them anew.

Fairer than the dawning of the day, radiant as the sun, as beautiful as the rainbow after the storm was the look that now lighted the craggy old face. Gone was the fierceness from the eyes. They blazed with joy. The voice that had grated and growled now whispered softly, "Oh, preacher, preacher! I feel I have just come alive."

"You have, my friend, you *have!*"

From across the room came a stifled sob. The wife who had prayed so hard, yearned so deeply for this hour flung herself down beside the bed, her face on the gnarled old hand on the sheet. "My darling," she cried, "at last, at last." A lovelier face the Pastor never saw than the face that lifted now, glowing with praise. "Thank You, Lord. Thank You."

This was all she could manage to say. But what more was needed?

It was more than a year later that the Pastor learned the final act of the drama. The telephone rang in the study one day. A woman's voice which he did not recognize at first spoke, "Maybe you do not remember me or my husband. I am Mrs. Graham, the wife of the man you visited in the hospital months ago. Do you remember that day he found Christ?"

"I could never forget that day."

"Well," she continued, "you will remember that he told you on other occasions when you stopped by to see him while he was in the hospital that as soon as he was physically able he would join the church he had attended for so many years. You will be glad to know that last night he kept his promise. It has taken all this time to recover his health and strength sufficiently to do it. Last night he stood before the congregation and told the people of that wonderful day when he gave himself to Christ and of how his entire life has changed. He is so different, so happy now. And again I want to thank you."

The Pastor knew that no thanks belonged to him. As he hung up the telephone moments later, he was saying in his heart, "Lord, I've seen You walk the aisle with so many. But I am thinking that last night You were especially proud of the one beside whom You stood. Thank You, Lord Jesus."

Then came Jesus — and the Pastor's heart was aglow.

11

THE WAYFARING
STRANGER

T HE SHRILL RINGING of the telephone cut like a scalpel
through the heavy curtain of sleep and jerked the Pastor to
half wakefulness. His fumbling hand reached out in the
darkness, grasping for the receiver. His voice sounded
strange to his own ears as he found the instrument and lifted
it. He spoke into it, still only half conscious. "Hello," he
said, his voice gravelly and indistinct. Clearing his throat he
tried again. "Hello."

The only sound that came over the wire was that of a
labored breathing, as though someone had run a long distance to get to the telephone and now was too exhausted, too
breathless to speak.

"Hello," the Pastor called out again, fully alert now.
"Are you there? Can you hear me? Can I help you?"

There was a soft whisper at the other end of the connection, a whimper like a wounded thing — desperate, frantic.
Again there was no sound but the labored breathing. And
then, "O God — O God — O God — O God."

Every nerve and fibre of the Pastor's being was alive now. Someone was in need — a need so deep and terrible it was the travail of agony seeking deliverance. His heart yearned over the unseen, unknown sufferer and he breathed a prayer, "O Lord, please let me help this person."

The sound of a strangled sob came over the wire and then a long shuddering sigh that ended with, "Are you a minister?"

"Yes," the Pastor replied. "Can I help you?" He put his whole heart into the question, suspecting that at any moment the connection might be broken.

The voice became clearer and more controlled. "Sir, I must apologize for calling you at 2 o'clock in the morning, but you see, I am desperate. I had definitely decided that I would kill myself tonight, but I got scared and for the present I can't do it. I dialed the operator and asked her to connect me with a minister. I am a stranger in your city and do not know any preachers personally. I don't know why she selected you, but I want to ask you, Sir, can you help me? Oh, please, please, can you help me?"

Realizing that the man who had been speaking was losing his self-control again and that a life might well be in the balance, the Pastor answered quietly, "I believe I can, or at least I *know* Someone who can. Where can I see you so that we can talk face to face?"

"I am in the bus depot," came the answer. "But I don't want to get you out at this hour. Perhaps if you could just tell me now one word of hope, one thing worth living for, I can make it all right and —"

"No, I want to talk to you personally," the Pastor interrupted. "I will be at the bus depot within half an hour. Tell me your name and something about your looks so I can find you."

There was an edge of bitterness in the short stiff laugh that answered him. "Preacher, just look for the ugliest man in the place. You won't have any trouble locating me by that

167

description. Anyway, my name is John Harrold and I am wearing a white jacket.''

''I'll tell you what I will do,'' the Pastor suggested. ''Suppose that if I don't see you, I go to the ticket office and have you paged. When your name is called, you meet me there and we will go somewhere and talk. And, Mr. Harrold, don't leave before I get there. You have asked for help and I know where you can get it. So you stay there and I will see you in a few minutes.''

There was a hurried clumsiness in the Pastor's hands as he drew on his clothes. The sudden awakening, the desperate urgency in the pleading voice to which he had just listened, the knowledge that John Harrold might walk out into the night and never be seen or heard from again lent desperation to every movement. Actually he dressed in record time, although it seemed to him that it took an hour. When the task was completed, he paused only long enough to pick up the worn New Testament from the desk in the hallway and out into the night he plunged.

A chilling rain greeted him as he hurried to his car, but he scarcely noticed it. His thoughts were all for a man who even at that moment might be walking the city streets, headed for a lonely rendezvous with death.

The tires of the car hummed on the wet pavement as the Pastor sped through the silent, empty streets. Even faster, the anxious questions charged through his mind. Who was this desperate man? What had he done so awful that he could no longer live with it? Would he wait? Could he be convinced that suicide was not the answer? ''O, Saviour,'' the Pastor groaned, ''O, Saviour, keep him there. Prepare his heart so I can tell him of Thee. Thou canst help him, I know. Just give me a chance at him, Lord. I know Thou wilt do the rest.''

Never was a sight more welcomed than the flashing neon sign that marked the bus depot. Quickly the Pastor found a parking space and headed for the door on the run. As he

168

entered the waiting area his eyes swept over the huge room. A sizeable group of people was there. A few of them were trying to sleep on the battered benches that lined the room. Others sat or stood about reading, their faces reflecting more boredom and impatience than interest in the pages before them. A child whimpered timidly and the soothing voice of his mother crooned comfortingly as she patted the weary, drooping head nestled upon her shoulder. The Pastor's hurried glance leaped from one figure to another, touching each one momentarily. His heart beat wildly with disappointment; nowhere in the room was there a man wearing a white jacket.

In anguish he said half aloud, "I'm too late. He has gone." Yet, there remained the hope that the man was somewhere about. He would have his name called out. His hurrying steps rang with hollow urgency as he covered the space to the ticket window in great strides.

The man behind the iron grill at the office did not even glance up. His pudgy form slouched lazily in the swivel chair, eyes glued to a newspaper spread out on the desk before him. His face was round and ruddy. Heavy lensed glasses only half concealed the bulging eyes that blinked rapidly as he read. His florid jaws worked rhythmically on a wad of gum. "Can I help you, sir," he asked with a bored voice, that obviously carried with it, "I hope not."

The Pastor's answer was crisp with impatience as he requested, "I wish you would page a Mr. John Harrold for me on your public address system, please."

With a sign of disgusted resignation the ticket agent leaned over, picked up the microphone and began to call, "Mr. John Harrold, please report to the ticket window. John Harrold, come to the ticket window."

As the amplified sound boomed throughout the high vaulted room, the Pastor was again looking eagerly over the people there. Some looked up with brief interest or annoyance at the loud disturbance, but no one moved.

169

Again the minister's heart sank. This was his last hope of finding the person who needed him. There was no conclusion now except that John Harrold had changed his mind or else had grown as tired of waiting as he was tired of living and had disappeared into the black wetness of the night. Disappointment weighed heavily upon the Pastor as he started to move away. In mid-stride he halted. His heart leaped. At his elbow a voice so low that it was almost inaudible was asking, "Are you the minister I talked to, sir?"

Half fearful lest his hearing had tricked him and holding his breath, the Pastor turned. There was the white jacket before him. Here was John Harrold. As he took a step toward the man and extended his hand, his eyes swept with swift practice over the figure confronting him. The man was of slight build. His body was painfully thin, slightly stooped as if an unseen load pressed down upon it. His clothes were clean but obviously old. The white jacket had probably been at one time another shade, but much cleaning had bleached it. The dark trousers, hanging baggily from the slim waist, were well worn.

However, it was the man's face that attracted the Pastor's gaze like a magnet. Seldom has he looked upon a more intriguing countenance. It defied description. It was strikingly handsome, and yet there was about it a hardness and a cruelty that made its expression almost pure evil. There was about it a rugged strength, and at the same time there was a helplessness written there. Beyond a doubt, ambition and hope had once made that face eager. Now hope and ambition were gone; only emptiness was left. Deep lines of suffering were etched into the thin face as though the beating of many storms of emotion and showers of tears had eroded the contours of the features. His hair was crisp and wiry and snow white. It was the look in the dark eyes that clutched at the Pastor's heart. They pleaded, they yearned, they cringed, they wept with unshed tears as the Pastor looked into them. A

170

rush of pity flooded the heart of the man of God as he completed his quick inventory.

His voice was gentle and assuring as he gripped the long hand that met his. "I am the pastor you called awhile ago. Where were you? I didn't see you anywhere in the waiting room and I had given up hope of finding you and was about to leave."

The pathetic eyes shifted their intent gaze and became downcast as John Harrold said in the same soft, monotonous voice, "I am glad you did not go, sir. I was outside walking up and down on the loading platform. You got here quicker than I expected." He looked up humbly. "Again I apologize for calling you out on such a night and at this hour. I would not have done it if there had been any other hope."

For a moment he paused and looked frantically at the man before him as though he expected the minister to turn away from him.

The thought came to the Pastor, *I guess you have been kicked around so much, you can't accept the fact that someone is willing to listen and waiting to help you.* Aloud he said, "Come on, John. Let's find a seat where we can talk."

In spite of the lateness of the hour and the sparsity of the crowd in the waiting room, it was not a simple matter to find a secluded spot. Each one of the long benches had at least one occupant. The two men walked slowly toward a corner that offered the most privacy. John followed at the Pastor's elbow, his steps short and quick as though he expected to resort to flight at any moment. His handsome face wore a look of abject misery. In the harsh glare of the overhead lights his eyes appeared hollowed; the weariness and depth were more pronounced upon the drawn countenance.

The Pastor settled down upon the bench and motioned for John Harrold to be seated at his side. "Now, son, tell me about your troubles," he said in a gentle, persuasive voice.

For a long moment the man beside him sat hunched over,

his hands clasping and unclasping as he stared vacantly at the floor. Again the Pastor spoke, "John, there may be a way out. Why don't you just start talking and let whatever is in your heart come out?"

His companion looked up swiftly, a mocking light sweeping his features. "Preacher," he said simply, "that would take all night. You never met anyone with a heart as full of hate and bitterness as mine."

The minister smiled, "I've got all night if you have. Just go ahead and pick a place to start. I'll listen no matter how long it takes."

"There just doesn't seem to be any beginning place," John stated with a weary sigh. "As far back as I can remember, I have had trouble. When I was just a kid I got kicked around. I was always fighting and getting beat up."

"Why?" the Pastor broke in. "Who kicked you around so much?"

"Aw — all the bigger kids in the neighborhood were after me all the time. My mom used to say I was the best looking boy in the neighborhood and she tried to keep me dressed up. You know, hair combed and clothes spic and span — that sort of thing. I guess they were jealous or something. They called me 'Pretty Boy' and they called me 'Duke' and 'Your Majesty' whenever they saw me. You know how kids pick on somebody who looks or acts a little different. They would try to mess me up, even threw me in mud holes sometimes. I used to get furious. I would get so mad I would cry. That made them really get on me, and then I would just see red and fly at them no matter how big they were or how many.

"That went on all the time; almost every day it happened. After awhile I got tired of it and made up my mind that I would make them respect me. So I started making plans."

He cast his dark eyes toward the Pastor, lifting his eyebrows quizzically as he asked, "You know how it is? You can't get people to respect you for your looks or your size or

172

ability or any of those things, so you find another way. At least, I did it. And my way was the wrong way. I made up my mind that if I couldn't be the biggest, I could be the meanest. If I couldn't make them look up to me any other way, I would be the wildest kid in the neighborhood. So I started out. I did everything I could to make the other boys notice me. I sassed the teachers at school. I made myself obnoxious to everybody. I threw rocks at the cops. I stole bicycles, then automobiles. I played up to the girls, especially the ones who had a reputation for being bad or wild.''

He paused for a moment and the jeering laugh that broke forth was like a croak. "I guess they were the only kind I could make a hit with. Yeah, I know now that's the way it was.'' John's eyes were pensive as he dredged up more bitter, distasteful memories.

"Preacher, by the time I was fifteen, I had slept with a dozen girls like that. And I had a reputation. Oh, they noticed me then. Those same guys who once messed me up, began to cross the street when they saw me coming. I carried a knife with me always and they knew I would use it. It didn't take long to get into trouble with the law. I had a police record before I was sixteen. But that didn't slow me up. I just made up my mind I wouldn't be stupid enough to get caught the next time. My mom and dad tried to stop me. Mom would talk to me and the tears would run down her poor face and she would cry over me until she just couldn't say any more — just sit there and look at me and sob until her heart would almost break.''

The tired voice choked momentarily. The Pastor laid his big hand soothingly on the bony shoulder beside him. The touch was enough to enable the young man to regain his self control. He brushed away the tears that coursed down his rugged face and resumed.

"About that time, I started to hang out in the beer parlors and I started to drink. I would get all fired up and do the

173

craziest things I could think of. And then I met a girl —''

John's drawl dwindled away, leaving the rest of the sentence suspended. A shy, beautiful smile touched his face, replacing the bitterness with a momentary eagerness. He lifted his head attentively as though he heard a beloved voice from somewhere. His eyes came alive as if they expected to behold a familiar form. For that brief span of time he was another person. Then, again, the harsh, bitter laugh of self-reproach erupted from the depths of remorse. His whole form seemed to fold up, all animation quickly gone, as he whispered, ''I messed that up, too.''

''Oh, we got married,'' he continued with a shrug of his shoulder. ''For awhile it seemed as though it would work. I got a job. We were happy. She was good for me.'' Suddenly, like a knife had ripped into his vitals, a cry of utter anguish was wrenched from his quivering lips, ''Why? why? why?'' he sobbed. He began to beat a fist into his hand.

''Preacher, why did everything turn sour and become rotten? Why did everything I touched or said or did become evil?''

His voice rose shrilly as he continued to pound his fist. People nearby turned to stare at them. A woman, obviously alarmed, hurriedly changed her seat. A man stretched out in sleep upon the adjoining bench roused up, looked wildly about him, mumbled a curse and sank wearily back to his slumber. John Harrold neither noticed nor cared that he had become the center of attention. The helpless sobbing continued uncontrolled, while his lean figure shook with the buffeting of the emotional storm raging in his soul.

The Pastor sat quietly for awhile knowing that it was better for the violence to expend itself in this fashion than in a more dreadful form. He sensed that a word at this point might be all that would be necessary to send this desperate man rushing out into the darkness to carry out his threat to end the life that held nothing but the dregs of shame and futility. Slowly, the shuddering form grew quieter. The fierce pounding of the fist had lost its vehemence. The Pastor relaxed his tense vigilance, realizing that John would not run now, that he would stay to cleanse his soul.

At last Harrold spoke again. His words were rabbling and then incoherent and the Pastor could make no sense from what he said. Now he ventured a suggestion. "John," he said easily, "let's get back to what you were telling me. What about the girl? You said you married her and were happy for a time. What happened?"

At his words, John turned suddenly and asked, "How can you sit here and listen to the life history of a bum like me?"

"You are no bum," the Pastor replied, "not to me, at any rate. To me you are a man — a man who has lost his way and wants to find it again, but still a man. I am not tired of listening. So tell me about the girl and the marriage."

"Can I even tell you?" Weariness filled the voice again. Then, "Yes, I suppose I can, and I must. There is no use withholding any part of it, is there? Well, like I said, everything was fine for awhile — I guess for a year or more. Then I got tired of coming home to the same house, the same face, the same boring life."

His eyes became ugly and a snarling tone made the words ugly also. "I got sick of it — sick to death of it. That's when I started running around again." This last was spoken defiantly. "But my wife tried to tie me down. I can't stand being ruled. I've got to be free."

"Are you free now, John?" the Pastor asked with a frown.

The white head bowed before him was flung up angrily. John's eyes flashed. "I am free to do with my life whatever I want, even to snuffing it out, preacher. And don't you forget it." For a moment he glared, but his eyes wavered and the defiance fled before the steady gaze of the minister. "No sir," he admitted more quietly, "I am not free now." He

175

turned away from the Pastor petulantly.

The Pastor spoke bluntly, "Go ahead with your story, John. I want to hear the rest of it."

"Well," John answered, "I started going out with other women. And for awhile I tried to cover it up, but my wife did a lot of crying and begging, and finally I got fed up with that, too. So I didn't make any pretense after that. I told her what I was doing." He was crying himself now. "Preacher, I flaunted it in her face. I rode by the house with other women in the car. I deliberately went to the most public places and made scenes so she would be bound to hear of it. I even took up with a woman in the house next to ours and she knew what I was doing because she could see it with her own eyes."

The tears flowed freely as John strangled in his own remorse. The veins stood out at his temples. His white head shook back and forth, back and forth in the anguish of a dreadful regret. "How could I get so rotten, fall so low? She was the only decent thing that I ever had and I destroyed it. Oh, how could I become such a fool?"

Dumb with misery himself, the Pastor could not answer. He mutely waited for the words to come again.

"Preacher, she left me after that. She went to live with her folks and took the two children we had. That is when I began to see what I had done. I begged her to forgive me and let me have another chance, but it was no use. I went into the army for a couple of years and when I came back, I found she was going with another man. She divorced me and married him about two weeks ago."

He gritted his teeth and bit off the next words. "The day I heard it, I swore I would kill her. Four days ago I left my home town with a gun in my pocket. I was going to hunt her down and kill both of them when I laid eyes on them. But for some reason I cannot explain, when I stopped here to transfer buses, I couldn't go on. I have been in your city three days now, just walking the streets, losing my mind, and tonight I decided there was no hope, no point in living any longer. I wish now I had killed myself instead of getting that operator to call you. All I have done is mess up the night for you.''

Even as he spoke the closing words, John Harrold was struggling to his feet. His gangling frame loomed over the Pastor as he stuck out his hand. ''Mr. Preacher,'' he said humbly, ''thank you for listening. I'll be going now.''

He pressed the Pastor's hand quickly and started to turn away. The minister was on his feet in a flash. He reached out and caught John's arm as he turned. ''Wait a minute, son,'' he demanded. ''I have listened to you until I heard you out. Don't you think you owe me a chance now? How about sitting down again and this time, you do the listening?'' A warm grin that accompanied the insistence in his voice made it a firm invitation rather than a command. The forlorn figure before him hesitated, even pulled back. The Pastor pursued with his friendliness. ''What have you got to lose, John? The night is about gone anyway, and, besides, there may be some answers.''

Reluctantly the man moved toward the bench again. He brushed a hand through his crisp white hair and retorted, ''There are no answers, preacher — just troubles, problems.''

With guarded words the Pastor began. Somehow the wall of rebellion and self-pity with which John Harrold had shut the world out and shut himself in, with only his misery for a companion, had to be breached. Somehow this lonely man had to find the Pastor's Friend.

The Pastor's words probed for some opening in the hard shell of an aching soul. He asked questions to clarify some of the story John had told him. The answers were given disinterestedly. Harrold had taken refuge in apathy. He considered the effort wasted. To him there were no answers, there was no hope. Besides, he had already concluded that the minister's apparent interest and desire to help was nothing more than a way to delay him in his intentions of ending his life. His words were mumbled, his tired face blank. He did not know that the minister was skillfully probing for an unguarded spot in his wall of self-pity, that his eager eyes watched intently for some response that would mark a place of beginning on the long road back. At last the Pastor's questions had marched around the wall. He had taken careful note of everything as he searched. And then he began.

"I wonder if *this* boy's name could have been John, too. Listen.

> A certain man had two sons: and the younger of them said to his father, Father, give me the portion of goods that falleth to me. And [his father] divided unto them his living. And not many days after the younger son gathered all together and took his journey unto a far country, and there wasted his substance with riotous living. And when he had spent all, there arose a mighty famine in that land and he began to be in want. And he went and joined himself to a citizen of that country and he sent him into his fields to feed the swine. And he would fain have filled his belly with the husks that the swine did eat: and no man gave unto him.[1]

"Do you recognize that young fellow, John?" His eyes bored into Harrold's eyes as he asked the question.

There was a spark of interest as the young man replied, "I guess I do, preacher. That sounds like my story. I reckon whoever that guy was, he felt about like I do. It just isn't worthwhile when you have fouled up everything. What did he do, hang himself?" A short scornful laugh was like a bark of derision bursting from his taut lips. "Or did he just drown himself in the muck of the hog pen?" he added sarcastically.

The Pastor remained unruffled by the scornfulness of his companion. There was no resentment in his voice as he replied, "No, John. He could have, if he had wanted to take that way out. But he didn't. Hear the next part of the story.

And when he came to himself, he said, How many hired servants of my father's have bread enough and to spare, and perish with hunger! I will arise and go to my father and will say unto him, Father, I have sinned against heaven, and before thee, and am no more worthy to be called thy son: make me as one of thy hired servants. And he arose and came to his father."[2]

Here the Pastor's soft, low voice broke off quoting the beautiful parable of the Prodigal Son. He looked at John with a renewed intensity. His burning eyes held the young man's gaze almost as though he had been hypnotized.

"John, that other young fellow had come to the point to which you have come. He had reached the end of his road too. He had gone about as far down as he could get. He had fouled up everything, as you would say. What did he do? you asked. He just took an honest look at two things. First, that he had hit bottom, and second, that he didn't have to stay down. He could go back home, facing whatever came, and begin anew. He could return to his father, openly admitting, fully confessing that he had made a mess of his life and ask his father to give him another chance.

John's fascinated gaze broke away with a visible struggle. He shrugged his thin shoulders and retorted in a matter-of-fact way, "A fat chance I would have of going home to my old man. He would probably ask if I had come home to bum some more money, as I have done a thousand times, and then show me to the door. And I would not blame him one bit if he did."

While the flat voice had been speaking, the Pastor had been only half-listening. He felt instinctively that the time had come to introduce John Harrold to Jesus. He too was talking, talking to his Friend. "O, Lord," his heart whispered, "Thou hast heard it all. Thou seest the need in this boy's heart and life. Lord Jesus, come now and knock at the door of this bitter heart. I will try my best to persuade him to open that door."

Aloud he said, "Perhaps your father would feel as you have said, John. But I know Someone who would not turn you away. I have a Friend who would be delighted to have you turn to Him for all that you need." The deep set eyes were all interest now. The thought that the minister had a friend who might be good for a handout was an appealing one. His face fell when the Pastor added, "My Friend's name is Jesus. And, John, if you would just turn to Him as the prodigal turned to his father, you would have every need of your soul and life filled."

The grim young face twisted and the bite of the old scorn sharpened the reply, "Preacher, you are wasting your breath. A guy like me hasn't got a chance, and you know it. Why, man, I have broken every law in the book. Do you think He would have the likes of me?"

"Listen again, John," was the Pastor's quiet retort. "Here is the next part of that other young man's story.

> And he arose, and came to his father. But when he was yet a great way off, his father saw him, and had compassion, and ran, and fell on his neck, and kissed him!"[3]

As he thrilled again within his own heart to the love and compassion of God, the Pastor's words became warm and eager. They spilled over each other, pushing one aside in the hurry to invade a stubborn heart and subdue it.

> And the son said unto him, Father, I have sinned against heaven and in thy sight, and am no more worthy to be called thy son. But the father said to his servants, Bring forth the best robe, and put it on him; and put a ring on his hand, and shoes on his feet: and bring hither the fatted calf and kill it; and let us eat, and be merry: for this my son was dead and is alive again; he was lost and is found.[4]

"John, don't you see? *Don't you see?* This thing can happen to *you*. You have but to come to God, to tell Him you're sorry for your sins as you have told me, ask Him to orgive and to let you start anew. It's for *you,* John. It's for you!''

And then came Jesus — His presence was just *there*. The minister thrilled in every part of his being, even John Harrold could not fail to sense His nearness.

The moment was breathless. Every fibre of the minister's body was taut, every nerve and muscle strained, so great was his desire to see a life made new as it was surrendered to God. The veins on the back of his tightly clenched hands stood out like ropes and perspiration beaded his forehead. The straining eagerness in his form shouted with a voiceless appeal — ''Please, please, please! Now, John, now!'' Like a mother watching breathlessly the first faltering step of her baby, like a lover waiting for an answer to his proposal, like the vigilance of an eagle stirring up her nest, the Pastor watched and waited for an answer.

And it came. It was a crushing final ''No.'' It was the Pastor's turn to slump dejectedly now. His heart plummeted. Tears stung his eyes. His face contorted with sorrow.

Seeing the deep hurt his rejection and refusal had caused, John added gently, ''You see, preacher, I have done *some* things that I do not think will ever be forgiven.''

Hope surged again into the Pastor's heart. Perhaps a door was still open. Instantly he seized the opportunity. ''But, John, you have told me of nothing tonight that God cannot and will not forgive if you will seek His forgiveness.''

Even as he gave the assurance, a transition was slowly spreading over the strangely old face of the youth at his side. His eyes became glazed. The already thin lips narrowed to a mere slit. His whole countenance took on a terrible grimness. The slit of his mouth parted enough to grate out the words, ''My hands are bloody, preacher.'' He held them out, palms upward as though his terrified eyes could behold crimson stains, as though he expected the man of God to see the sight that was seared upon his own brain.

"I don't know how many men I have killed," he gritte
out. "My hands are bloody, bloody, bloody!"

It was a chant, an awful, aching sing-song of horror. Hi
whole world contained only two hands in that moment, tw
blood-stained hands that had killed. There was no thought i
his mind for his audience, for his surroundings, for anythin
but the dreadful scenes conjured up from deep in his soul. Hi
voice spoke with a hollow, spectral note.

"One night in Korea, I was on guard duty in a forwar
outpost. I was manning a machine gun. We had stretched
string with tin cans tied to it all around our position so that i
the enemy tried to slip on us in the darkness, he would touc
the string and the cans would give the alarm. I sat there in th
darkness thinking of home, of my wife, of a thousand things
Suddenly the cans began to clatter. I couldn't see a thing but
pulled the trigger on that machine gun and I swept it back an
forth. Above the noise of the gun I heard the scream — (
God, they screamed and screamed. A grenade explode
nearby and I was hit, but I kept on sweeping that gun bac
and forth. I don't know how long it lasted. Somebod
brought a light and all I could see was dead bodies, bleedin
bodies, groaning bodies, screaming bodies."

His face was ghostly now, pale and sick and terrible. "
don't know how many of them died there on that hillside. Th
bodies were piled up, crisscrossed like sticks of wood. And
killed them. I murdered those guys. They wanted to live a
much as I did, but I snuffed them out. And they gave me
medal for it. They called me a hero and read me a citation an
pinned a hunk of tin on my shirt. But that didn't erase th
memory of those poor, dead guys I had killed. That didn'
wash the blood off my hands."

The voice broke with emotion. It became a quiet, hopeles
sobbing that racked John's lean figure so that it writhed an
twisted in agony.

The Pastor's whole heart was in the response as he said

"Even *that* God will forgive, John. I can imagine how you feel about that night, about the blood you say is on your hands. But, my Friend shed His blood on the cross so those stains could be removed. Nothing else, no one else can do that for you. He can! He will!''

John Harrold arose from the bench. There was an air of finality about his stance, his whole attitude, as he stood over the preacher. "I thank you again, Sir,'' he said, "but this is something I have to work out for myself. Religion is not the answer for me.'' The Pastor opened his mouth to speak but John's uplifted hand of protest shut off the words.

"No, preacher,'' he said again with finality, "I know what you would tell me, but your Christ is not the answer for me either. I am going now. Please do not try to stop me or follow me.''

Seeing the fear that sprang into the Pastor's face, he smiled gently, his own face made almost sweet by the rare smile. "I promise you I will not take my own life tonight. You have given me something to think on. Perhaps you will hear from me again.'' Abruptly he turned, and before the Pastor could rise to his feet was swiftly gone out into the night.

The Pastor slept little during the tag end of the night. What rest he got was broken by dreams that haunted him when he awakened. There was not an hour of the days that followed that he did not breathe a prayer for John Harrold. It was about twilight, three days later, that he was called to the phone again. Immediately he recognized John's voice, and his heart leaped with joy. He would have another chance!

But it was not to be. The voice coming through the instrument said, "Pastor, there is no use of going on. I can't stand it any longer.'' There was a click as the wire went dead. So did the Pastor's hope and joy. He stood stunned, holding the receiver in his hand and staring at it blankly, unable to believe or accept what he had heard. Finally, a long, shuddering sigh of despair was torn from him. His heart was burdened under the weight of sorrow. Gently placing the phone on its cradle, he went out into the gathering darkness, feeling now the urgent need to walk and to talk to his Friend.

To the west a storm cloud reared high upon the horizon like a great black-robed giant, marching eastward with relentless tread.

From time to time the lightning whipped its flaming sword across the sky, the thunder pealed. The Pastor walked toward the storm. Sudden gusts of wind tore at him, but they went unnoticed. They were insignificant compared to the winds of sorrow that shrieked over his barren heart. The first, big cold drops of rain pelted his face and went unfelt. His face was already wet with tears.

Then came Jesus! He whispered to the Pastor's aching heart, "I know what you feel. I understand." Together they walked toward the storm and talked of another time when the heavens grew dark — talked of Calvary.

[1]Luke 15:11-16
[2]Luke 15:17-20a
[3]Luke 15:20
[4]Luke 15:21-24